good
fish
guide

Bernadette Clarke
Marine Conservation Society

MARINE CONSERVATION
SOCIETY

The UK Charity dedicated to the protection of the marine environment
and its wildlife

Marine Conservation Society
9 Gloucester Road
Ross-on-Wye
HR9 5BU
Tel: 01989 566017
www.mcsuk.org

Citation: Good Fish Guide. B Clarke (2002).
Marine Conservation Society, Ross-on-Wye. UK.

ISBN No: 0-948150-31-9

Printed by
Severnprint Limited, Gloucester
on Totally Chlorine Free Paper
Telephone: 01452 416391

Contents

Marine Conservation Society

The Marine Conservation Society (MCS) is the UK's national charity dedicated to the protection of the marine environment and its wildlife. MCS works to highlight threats to both marine wildlife and to the wider marine and coastal environment on which so many livelihoods depend.

In order to protect our marine environment for this and future generations MCS takes action to:

- Increase awareness about marine life and the role of the marine environment in our lives through education and active involvement in conservation projects

- Protect important marine species and habitats

- Achieve ecologically sustainable management of fisheries

- Promote environmentally sensitive use of non-living marine resources

- Implement an integrated approach to the management of the coastal zone

- Eliminate pollution of the marine and coastal environment, from both land-based and offshore sources

Through education, volunteer participation and high profile campaigns, MCS brings marine conservation issues to the attention of the public, media, industry and Government alike. MCS promotes solutions to the many threats that face our seas by informing, involving and influencing those that have a responsibility for the marine environment. MCS informs, through the production of educational resources for all sectors from Primary school to working professionals. MCS involves individuals and communities in volunteer projects from marine life surveys to beach cleans and litter surveys. MCS influences decision makers at the highest level through reasoned argument based on sound factual evidence and scientific principles.

MCS supports the concept of sustainable management of fish stocks whilst recognising the impacts of fishing on the marine ecosystem and the impacts of other activities on fisheries.

www.mcsuk.org

Fishing for tuna

Acknowledgements

MCS would like to very much thank Derek Cooper for writing the foreword to this Guide and Martha Holmes for writing the introduction.

In particular MCS would like to thank our sponsors – Loch Fyne Marine Trust and PADI Project Aware without whose support the production of this Guide would not have been possible.

Loch Fyne Marine Trust was established to safeguard and enhance the biodiversity of Loch Fyne – the longest sea loch in Scotland – and is committed to supporting and protecting Loch Fyne, its ecology and surrounding coastal communities. The Trust is funded by a levy on all home delivery orders placed with Loch Fyne Oysters Ltd.

In response to the growing awareness of the problems facing both ocean and freshwater ecosystems, PADI (Professional Association of Diving Instructors) founded Project AWARE (Aquatic World Awareness, Responsibility and Education). Project AWARE seeks to increase, through education, both the diving and non-diving communities' environmental awareness and to encourage responsible interactions between humans and the aquatic environment.

MCS thank the Esmée Fairbairn Charitable Trust for their support during the initial research period.

MCS would also like to thank Paul Kay for allowing us to use his wonderful photographs to illustrate the text. All photographs are © Paul Kay except those listed in the photo credits on page 192. Paul Kay is a professional photographer who runs the Marine Wildlife Photo Agency which specialises in temperate marine life. He is a passionate marine conservationist and can be contacted at paul@marinewildlife.co.uk

MCS would also like to thank the following individuals and organisations for their contributions to the Guide. In particular we would like to thank Dr Mike Pawson, Centre for Environment, Fisheries and Aquatic Science (CEFAS), Dr Stephen Lockwood, Coastal Fisheries Conservation & Management (CFCM), Professor Alasdair McIntyre, University of Aberdeen, Caroline Pollack, World Conservation Union (IUCN) and Dr John Webster, Scottish Quality Salmon (SQS) for their assistance and contributions on the scientific and technical aspects of the text.

Also many thanks to the following people for providing very useful comments and contributions on the first draft: Simon Waterfield, Andy Lane, Cliff Morrison, Bruce Whitehall, Samantha Fanshawe, Kate Hutchinson, Richard Harrington, Peter Richardson, Ann Hunt, Jeremy Hooper, Andrew Mallison, Paolo Bray, Mark Palmer, Mark Berman, Andrew Bing, Carol Harris, Dr Eric Edwards, Dr Peter Hunt, Brian O'Riordan, Jeremy Langley, Sheelagh Johnson, Malcolm Gilbert, Ben Mullins, Richard Van de Peer, James Bell, Mary Stuart, Hansen Black, Dick James, John Martinek, Mark Shayler, Iain Mahood, David Rose, Vicky Wichard, Carol Harns, John Harmen, Iian Young, Phil Brook, Tim Cartwright-Taylor and Doreen Hillyer. Thanks to Nicola Mitchard and John Smith for their assistance with initial research for the Guide.

Foreword

Since early days the common assumption has been that there would always be plenty of fish in the sea. Few of us could have foreseen the damage that increasing industrialization of fisheries has caused, enabling us to sweep our seas clean of fish, including once common species such as cod and skate. Just as we have paid farmers not to farm so we are now contemplating paying fishermen not to fish. While good husbandry of our land is an important issue at the top of the political agenda, management of our seas and fishstocks is less ambitious.

When we think of fish many consumers automatically think of cod and haddock. Because of relentless over-fishing of these species over the years supplies are not as bountiful or as reliable as they once were. As stocks of white fish decline, and fish prices increase, processors think of ever more inventive ways to eke out supplies and keep costs down by forming it into various shapes, bolstered with crumbs and additives. Fish fingers may be convenient and easy to eat but they are not much of a nutritional bargain.

But all is not yet lost. Despite our over-reliance on cod and haddock there are plenty more species to choose from. The *Good Fish Guide* lists more than 60 species, many of which are not yet over-fished. Consumers can help conserve fish stocks by reducing demand for over-exploited species such as cod, haddock and plaice and diversifying their tastes towards less exploited species. We can also support communities dependent on fishing for their livelihoods by buying fresh fish from local suppliers. Often this fish is landed from small day-fishing boats.

The *Good Fish Guide* also raises awareness of other issues – both environmental and social – associated with eating seafood. We can continue to eat fish by ensuring that fish remain in the sea and avoid eating the most endangered or vulnerable species. We can choose fish that has been caught using methods that cause less damage to the marine environment, such as fish and shellfish taken by lines and in traps or pots instead of huge trawl nets which engulf all in their path, including dolphins, or by gears that plough up the seabed.

The *Good Fish Guide* is the most comprehensive guide yet for consumers concerned with the impacts of eating seafood on the marine environment. It may not provide all the answers but it asks all the right questions!

Derek Cooper, writer and broadcaster. Creator and presenter of BBC Radio 4 Food Programme from October 1979 to December 2001.

Derek Cooper (left) at Billingsgate fish market

Introduction

The oceans contain the most diverse habitats on our planet. But because of the costs and physical difficulties of working underwater, our understanding of ocean ecosystems is, relatively speaking, still in its infancy. Nevertheless, it is crucial that we recognise and accept how essential the oceans are to the well-being of life on Earth. Marine microscopic plants provide the oxygen we breathe and the seas that surround us help to regulate the life-sustaining temperatures we take for granted. We also know that beneath the waves the oceans support an astounding array of life-forms, many of which we have yet to discover let alone understand. With this knowledge, Man should, I believe, treat the oceans with caution and care rather than with flagrant disrespect.

The seas have been a source of food for time immemorial but it has now become painfully clear that fish stocks in many oceans are under threat. Our approach to exploitation must therefore change. Among the many impacts affecting life in the oceans are industrial pollution, agricultural run-off, and habitat destruction. But it is increasingly clear that the most consistent cause of stock depletion is over-fishing. We can no longer ignore this fact.

The problems of over-fishing are numerous. The method maybe unselective, involving the killing of young fish (and a large by-catch of unwanted animals) as well as the targeted adults. The method may destroy a habitat which the targeted fish depends on. Or, as new high-tech equipment is employed, the method may have become too 'efficient', leaving too few fish to sustain the population. Nevertheless, in the minefield of fishing ethics, there are some fisheries that emerge as being well-managed, whose stocks are sustainable. How then do we find out about them?

The *Good Fish Guide* comes at a critical time and has an important role to play in our lives. Many people are aware of the over-fishing problem, but would like to learn about the bigger picture and know how they can make a difference as consumers. The guide will answer most of their questions. Moreover it will increase people's awareness of the diversity of fish that are caught, mistakenly or otherwise. This greater understanding will, I hope, stimulate concern for the plight of the endangered species before it is too late to save them. The guide is important, accurate and essential reading for those who care about the future of the oceans.

Dr Martha Holmes, BBC Natural History Unit, Bristol

Martha Holmes has worked for the BBC's Natural History Unit since completing her PhD on fish behaviour. On joining the Unit she has presented numerous programmes including *Reefwatch* (a live underwater broadcast from the Red Sea), *Splashdown* and *Sea Trek*. As a producer she has travelled the globe to make many award-winning films such as *Life in the Freezer, Hippos out of Water, Otters - the Truth, Wildlife Special - Polar Bear* and more recently the celebrated series *The Blue Planet*. She presented the *Blue Planet* environmental programme *Deep Trouble* which addressed the impacts of over-fishing around the world.

Aims of the Guide

The supply chain of fish and fish products is complex, and for this reason it is not easy for consumers to make straightforward informed decisions about the species they are consuming.

The *Good Fish Guide* has been written to provide clear and unambiguous information on the range of issues associated with eating fish and is designed to promote the purchase and consumption of marine fish in the UK from sustainably managed fisheries (including farms) which seek to minimise environmental, ecological and social damage.

If you like to eat seafood, but are concerned about the impact this may have on stocks, marine wildlife and habitats the *Good Fish Guide* will help you choose fish which:

- Come from healthy stocks
- Are sustainably managed
- Are caught using methods which minimise damage to the environment
- Are from fisheries which do not harm wildlife
- Support UK and local fishing communities

The Guide also aims to encourage producers and retailers to provide more comprehensive labelling, including details on area and method of capture, in order that consumers can make more informed choices about the fish that they buy.

Bycatch of Dogfish and other species in Nephrops catch

Chapter One
Buying and Eating Fish

Introduction

Fish is very versatile and one of the most nutritious foods we can eat. It can be steamed, baked, grilled, smoked, poached, marinated, boiled, micro-waved, fried or even eaten raw. A great variety of seafood - more than 60 species of fish and shellfish - is found in UK waters. Some of the finest shellfish in the world are caught around the coasts of Britain, from scallops and cockles to shrimp and lobster.

The fish we eat

The major division in the fish we eat is between finfish and shellfish.

Finfish may be further divided into those with bones, bony fish or teleosts (cod, herring, plaice and haddock etc.), and those without – cartilaginous fish or elasmobranchs (skates, sharks and dogfish). 98% of landings of fresh fish in the UK are bony fish.

White fish

White fish, so called because of their white flesh, are divided into two groups: round and flat fish. Round fish such as cod, whiting, haddock and coley are usually sold as steaks, fillets or cutlets. Large flat fish species include halibut and turbot, whilst smaller species include plaice, lemon sole and Dover sole.

The best known species of cod in Britain is *Gadus morhua*, the Atlantic cod. Due to decades of over-fishing the Atlantic cod is now close to commercial extinction in the North Sea. However, only one fifth of the cod consumed in Britain is taken from this area. The remaining four fifths of cod eaten in Britain come from the waters of the Barents Sea, and the seas around Iceland and Norway. Other important white fish species include haddock, saithe, hake and plaice.

Oily fish

Oily fish are differentiated from white fish because they store their fat reserves in the flesh. In white fish, oil is concentrated or stored in the liver. Oil-rich fish include herring, mackerel, salmon and tuna.

Oily fish and white fish are also differentiated by their muscle type. Fish have two types of muscle fibre, red and white. Red muscle is used for sustained swimming and white muscle for 'burst' swimming. Mackerels and tunas which belong to the Scrombid family are fast swimming fish and have more red muscle than slower white fish species like cod and plaice.

Exotics

Unusual or brightly coloured fish, which may be white or oily fish, are generally described as 'exotics' and are imported from many tropical regions including the West Coast of Africa, the Seychelles and the Indian Ocean. Exotic fish, such as the swordfish and red snapper are becoming increasingly more popular, especially on restaurant menus. Other 'exotics' include species such as parrot fish, dorade, kingfish and groupers.

Shellfish

Shellfish is a broad term used for groups of invertebrate organisms which have a hard outer shell, although some individual species (such as the squid) may have an internal shell. Shellfish belong to one of three divisions (Phyla) in the animal kingdom; molluscs, arthropods or echinoderms. The Phylum Mollusca comprises seven classes, of which three, bivalves (scallop, oyster, mussels etc.); gastropods (whelks); and cephalopods (squid and octopus), are of particular commercial interest. The edible parts are commonly organs such as the digestive gland and gonads as well as muscle. In squid, only the muscular mantle and, occasionally, the tentacles are eaten.

The Phylum Arthropoda, the largest in the Animal Kingdom, is divided into a number of classes of which the Class Crustacea (crab, lobster, prawn, shrimp etc.) is the most important. Other less familiar shellfish such as starfish, urchins and sea cucumbers belong to the Phylum Echinodermata. Most shellfish live on or in the seabed and exhibit a wide variety of life-styles.

The two species which account for the majority of shellfish landings by the UK fleet are crabs (20%) and Nephrops (Dublin Bay Prawns) (21%). 27 and 29,000 tonnes of crab and Nephrops respectively were landed by UK boats in 2000, the majority of Nephrops come from the North Sea and crabs from the Western Channel.

Fish lifestyles
Finfish and shellfish are further classified according to where they are found in the water column, this is generally determined by their feeding habits.

Demersal fish tend to feed close to, or in some cases on, the seabed. This group represents just under half of all UK fresh fish landed in 2000. Of this group cod, haddock, plaice and whiting account for 52% whilst sole, saithe (or coley), ling and monkfish (or anglerfish) are important constituents of the rest. Demersal species are the most valuable species accounting for 59% of the value of UK landings.

Pelagic species tend to feed in mid-water. Herring and mackerel are the two main species accounting for 89% of UK pelagic landings. Although pelagic fish account for 24% of landings by quantity they account for only 5% by value.

Benthic species are those found in the seabed e.g. Nephrops or langoustines. Shellfish account for 27% of landings by quantity and 36% by value.

Deep-water fish
As stocks of more traditional species decline, fishermen are moving into deeper water in search of new fishing opportunities. Deep-water species are generally referred to as those found in waters greater than 400 metres. Because of their biological characteristics, deep-water fish are particularly vulnerable to overfishing and stock collapse.

Biological characteristics of deep-water fish

- Typically live in depths of between 400 and 1,700 metres
- Slow growing, long-lived with a relatively high age at first maturity
- Low fecundity and vulnerable to over-exploitation
- Stocks have low levels of sustainable yields
- If stocks are overfished they are likely to take many years to recover

The majority of deep-water species, especially the more unusual ones like rabbit fish, are destined for non-UK markets, in particular France. Deep-water species most commonly found for sale in the UK include orange roughy, blue ling, ling, halibut and monkfish, which is also found in shallower waters in seas covering the continental shelf (i.e. in waters less than 200 metres depth).

Orange Roughy

How much fish do we eat?

Fish consumption
In 2000, UK householders consumed 442,400 tonnes of fish. Individual consumption of fish has remained fairly constant over the past decade at approximately 143 g per person per week – half as much as was consumed in the late 1940s. This amounts to a weekly expenditure of 80 pence and represents just under 4% of all expenditure on food. Although fish is widely appreciated for being healthy and nutritious, barriers to increasing our consumption of fish have been identified as: difficult to prepare, handle and cook; for many health is not a primary concern; and competition from other diets e.g. vegetarianism.

On average, fish accounts for approximately 6% of the total protein intake of British adults. This is small compared to the 36% obtained from meat and 17% from milk and milk products. In contrast, the Japanese consume about three times as much fish as the British making them the highest fish-consuming nation in the world.

Fish expenditure
Whilst expenditure on beef and veal has decreased by 3 pence (5%) per person per week in the period 1992 to 2000, expenditure on fish (80.1 pence per person per week) and poultry (85.7 pence) has increased by 15% and 31% respectively.

Table 1: Average annual prices of fish (live weight) (Source: DEFRA 2001)

Species	£ per tonne 1970	£ per tonne 1990	£ per tonne 2000
Herring	32	119	103
Mussels	23	140	193
Mackerel	55	123	254
Haddock	66	1,043	1,018
Plaice	132	881	1,150
Cod	80	1,087	1,369
Hake	250	2,187	2,011
Nephrops	249	1,910	2,147
Lemon sole	278	1,824	2,497
Lobsters	1,262	8,246	10,030

Fish is no longer a cheap source of protein and now costs more than either meat or cheese. Since 1995 the price of fish has increased by 23% compared to the average price of milk, cheese and eggs, which have remained the same, and vegetables which have decreased in price by 9%.

Table 2: Household retail purchases of main species of fish and shellfish in Great Britain (Source: Seafish 2000)

Species	Purchases 2000 (tonnes)	% Change since 1994
Cod	64,207	- 23 %
Coley	4,469	+ 40 %
Haddock	32,840	- 14 %
Kippers (smoked herring)	5,821	- 28 %
Mackerel	7,557	+ 3 %
Other shellfish	4,473	+ 13 %
Plaice	6,432	- 43 %
Prawns/shrimp/scampi	24,540	+ 20 %
Salmon	22,721	+ 91 %
Trout	5,292	+ 3 %

Supply and demand

UK fish suppliers

The main fish suppliers in Britain include companies such as Young's Bluecrest Seafood, Birdseye Walls and Findus. With an annual turnover of £320 million, Young's Bluecrest is one of the top 20 food companies in the UK (discounting internationals such as Coca-Cola Schweppes etc) and is the biggest supplier of fish in the UK and possibly in Europe. As well as being the UK's principal added value fish product manufacturing company, with own brand Young's, the company also supplies many of the retailers and food service companies in their own brands as well. The company is also the largest buyer of cod in the UK and purchases in excess of 10,000 tonnes annually, principally from Norway and Iceland where stocks are well managed.

Supermarkets

As a result of changing consumer habits, many independent high street fishmongers have closed and been replaced by large supermarket chains which now account for about 80% of all retail sales of fresh fish and shellfish in the UK. This compares with just 10% in 1982. Major chains such as Tesco, Waitrose, Safeway, Asda, Sainsburys, and Morrisons now have extensive wet or fresh fish counters and sell a wide range of fish and fish products. Tesco has the largest market share of fresh and chilled fish and leads on both value (18.5%) and volume (20%). Fresh fish stalls and independent fishmongers are however not uncommon in market and coastal towns. Independent fishmongers have 15% of the share of fresh and chilled household purchases in Great Britain (see Figure 1). The ten most popular species, listed in Table 3, account for 80% of the retail value of chilled and fresh fish sold.

Figure 1: Market share of fresh and chilled fish (Source: AGB Superpanel 2001)

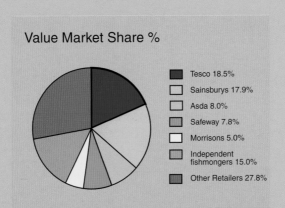

Table 3: Top 10 (chilled) species in retail value (£000s) (Source: AGB Superpanel 2001)

Rank	Species	2001	% Growth
1	Salmon	242,196	25
2	Haddock	136,070	5
3	Cod	115,836	13
4	Prawns	75,833	13
5	Other*	38,384	16
6	Plaice	32,699	6
7	Mackerel	31,742	11
8	Trout	31,467	13
9	Tuna	24,634	47
10	Sole	18,504	0

*   Other refers to minor species (e.g. Huss, John Dory, Mullet, etc) eaten in small amounts

Because domestic landings cannot meet total demand for white fish, we import more cod, haddock. saithe and plaice than are caught by UK registered vessels. The opposite is true for pelagic species, as we export most of the herring and mackerel landed and only a small proportion is eaten in the UK (see Table 4).

The highest demand for fresh domestic landings is from the wholesalers and independent fishmongers. Whilst more traditional outlets are happy to be supply-driven, fish supplies are subject to availability due to environmental

Market-town fish stall

conditions - supermarket chains, which are generally consumer-driven, insist on a reliable, continuous and consistent supply at competitive pricing. In order to maintain such a supply the multiples are obliged to import.

Restaurants and pubs

Seafood restaurants and pubs selling 'organic' or 'fish from substainably managed sources' are becoming more widespread and popular. UK based restaurant chains include Loch Fyne Restaurants, Fish!, Fishworks, Livebait and Harry Ramsdens.

Loch Fyne Restaurants, with 18 restaurants UK-wide, is the first British restaurant chain to take the inititive and remove species recommended as 'to be avoided' by MCS from its menus (see Table 8). Loch Fyne Restaurants and its founding company Loch Fyne Oysters have developed a standard – *Total Sustainability* – which undertakes to ensure that the environmental impact of the company's aquaculture activities i.e. mussel and oyster cultivation is at least neutral. The company also strives to harmonise fishing and aquaculture with the natural environment, biodiversity and provide skilled work in the community in line with local traditions.

The UK based restaurant chain Fish! became the first seafood restaurant chain in the world to use the Marine Stewardship Council (MSC) (see Chapter 2) logo on its menu.

Table 4: UK Imports and Exports for selected species for 2000
(Source: Seafish 2000)

Species	Imports (tonnes)	Imports (£'000s)	Exports (tonnes)	Exports (£'000s)
Dogfish	2,128	2,959	1,076	2,560
Haddock	37,441	78,755	1,195	3,489
Plaice	6,688	18,093	1,523	1,940
Saithe	4,821	6,080	2,384	1,899
Cod	121,235	310,051	8,512	17,134
Herring	4,741	1,934	49,697	14,386
Mackerel	5,519	1,803	90,341	39,944
Total	182,574	419,674	154,729	81,352

Marketing seafood

Seafish

The Seafish Industry Authority (Seafish) was established by the UK Government in 1981 and is a non-departmental public body. Seafish serves all sectors of the UK seafood industry, from fishermen and processors, to retailers, fish friers and consumers. Its main income is from a statutory levy on all sea fish and sea fish products landed and imported into the UK. The levy is used to fund a range of services to benefit the fishing industry. Services include campaigns

Market-town fish shop

to promote eating fish; training; research and development work, with the focus on developing marine finfish and shellfish cultivation techniques; developing more selective methods of fishing; improving safety at sea; and trying to reduce fish processing costs. Seafish also produces a range of literature on cooking and eating seafood. Their website www.seafish.co.uk is a comprehensive source of information for consumers and industry.

Seafood Scotland

Seafood Scotland was set up by the main representative bodies of the Scottish Seafood Industry to promote, market and develop Scottish fish. Its principle aim is to optimise the value of the Scottish seafood catch by improving its quality and reducing wastage.

Other initiatives for improving the quality and thus the value of declining fish resources include direct weighing at sea and 'traceability' (see Chapter 4).

Buying fish

Fresh fish

The Torry Scale is a system devised by the Torry Research Station in Aberdeen to score the freshness and quality of fish. Waitrose, for example, will never buy fish unless it achieves at least 8 out of a possible 10.

To ensure that the fish you buy is fresh and of good quality look out for the following:

- Whole fresh fish will have clear eyes that are bright and not sunken
- The skin should be shiny and moist - really fresh fish feels slightly slippery
- Bright red gills
- A sea-fresh aroma
- Natural colouring – colouring varies with diet and habitat type
- Scales should not be missing and they should be firmly attached to the skin
- Tails should be stiff and the flesh feel firm

- When buying white fish fillets look out for neat, trimmed fillets and a white translucent appearance

- If buying frozen fish, check that the fish is frozen solid with no signs of partial thawing

- Make sure that packaging is undamaged

- Smoked fish should look glossy with a fresh, smoky aroma

- Take care when selecting shellfish to choose shells which are tightly closed and without any gaps or cracks

(Source: Seafish 2001)

An additional point for consumers to consider when buying 'fresh' i.e. chilled fish, is to check whether it has been previously frozen. For example, cod on the ice display may have been in an Icelandic cold store for a year before being defrosted for sale. Some retailers such as Marks & Spencer guarantee that all their wet fish chilled products have never been previously frozen.

Frozen fish

Many fish are filleted and frozen at sea and are readily available from supermarket freezer cabinets, pre-prepared for immediate use. Breaded and battered portions form a large part of the market. The Frozen at Sea Fillets Association (FASFA) (see Chapter 2) reported increases of 22 and 27% in sales of frozen cod and haddock to processors, as consumers looked for alternative food products in the wake of the foot and mouth outbreak in 2001. All FASFA fish is frozen within 6 hours of being caught and is guaranteed fresh, of the highest quality and from well-managed fisheries.

Chilled fish products are an increasingly common sight in supermarkets and are often packaged in what are referred to as controlled (CAP) or modified atmosphere packaging (MAP) to increase shelf life.

Smoked fish may be either hot or cold smoked. The most common species to be smoked in Britain are cod, herring (kippers), haddock, mackerel, trout and salmon. The fish is salted in brine solution before being smoked. Cold smoked species include kipper and trout and require further cooking before being eaten. Hot smoked fish (e.g. mackerel and salmon) can be eaten directly without further preparation.

There are a variety of ready meals catering for single and two-person households in particular. Fish may also be purchased canned – mackerel, herring, anchovies, pilchards, sardines, tuna, crab, shrimp, prawns, mussels and oysters are all available in tins packed in either brine or oil, pickled or as dried salted fish. Value-added products (products where the original raw material is processed to increase value) such as fish-fingers, breaded scampi, fish-in-sauce, pies, bakes, crab sticks and salmon mousse are also becoming increasingly popular. Sales of value-added products during 2000 grew by 10% in value and 13% in volume. Fish-in-sauce products are the most popular product. It is worth noting, however, that the main constituents of many of these products are often cheaper ingredients such as potato and not fish!

By-products of fish processing

In addition to direct human consumption, an estimated 30-40% of world catch is converted to fishmeal and oil for the production of animal feed, fertiliser and the manufacture of products such as margarine and biscuits. Fish for non-human consumption is derived from targeted industrial fisheries and from offal and trimmings as a by-product of the (white) fish processing industry (see Chapter 5). A range of uses are made of particular by-products arising from fish processing (see Table 5).

Table 5: Lesser known by-products of fish processing

Product	Uses	Source
Chitin	To manufacture food wrapping, coagulants, drilling muds and photographic products	Shellfish shells
Chitosan	To purify drinking water	Shrimp shells
Chondroitia	Treatment of arthritis	Elasmobranchs
Gall-bladder	As a source of insulin	Fish digestive organ
Guaine	To make simulated pearls and items such as umbrella handles	Silver pigment layer beneath fish scales/skin
Isinglass	In the fining of wine and beer	Fish swim-bladders
Liver oil	As a source of vitamins A & D	Notably cod liver
Pyloric caeca	As a source of enzymes for washing powders	A digestive organ in the alimentary system of fish
Sepia	As a food dye. Also used in homeopathic medicine to treat hormone disorders in women.	Cuttlefish and squid ink
Skin & bone	To make glue and leather	Fish including elasmobranchs

Bream

Buying and eating fish abroad

To assist you in identifying fish when travelling and eating fish abroad a list of names for the most popular species likely to be encountered is included in Table 6. It should be borne in mind that in countries like Spain there is a culture of eating small or 'baby' fish. The eating of small, immature fish should be avoided at all times even if you are on holiday! France is a major destination for many of the deep-water species taken from the deep-water to the west of Britain in the north-east Atlantic. Many of these species, although unfamiliar to UK consumers, are vulnerable to exploitation and many stocks are over-fished.

Table 6: Naming fish abroad

English	French	Spanish	German
Angler/Monkfish	Baudroie or Loup (de mer)	Sapo	Seeteuful
Basking shark	Pelerin	Peregrino	Riesenhai
Bass	Bar Commun	Lubina	Seebarsch
Cod	Cabillaud	Brabos	-
Deep-water prawn	Crevette Nordique	Cameron	Tiefseegarnele
Haddock	Aiglefin/Eglefin	Eglefino	Schellfische
Hake	'chon/Morue cod	Pescadillo/Merluza	Meerhecht
John Dory	Zee	Pez de San Pedro	Petersfisch
Ling	Lingue Bleu	Maruca	Leng/Lingfische
Lobster	Homard	Lubrigante	Hummer
Prawn	Caramonte/Crevette	Quisquella	Krabbe
Rabbitfish	Chimere	Quimera	Seeratte
Ray/Skate	Raie	Raya	Rochen
Shark	Requin	Tibourne	Hai/Haifisch
Snapper	Vivaneau	-	Schnapper
Squid	Encornet	Jibia	Kalmar
Tuna	Thon	Atun	Thun/Thunfisch

Eating seafood

Guidelines on eating 'eco-friendly' fish

A number of guidelines have been produced by various organisations on avoiding eating certain species of fish, which because of either their biology and life-history characteristics, species status and/or the method of capture and/or the way they are managed or produced are more vulnerable to over-exploitation and therefore less sustainable than other species. Some rank species to indicate least (i.e. species to be avoided) and most sustainable species (see Table 7).

Table 7: Summary of guidelines on consuming 'eco-friendly' fish

Name of Organisation	Guideline/ Report details	Species to avoid (highest ranked only where applicable)
Audubon Society www.audubon.org	The Audubon Guide to Seafood - What's a fish lover to eat?	Shark; swordfish; orange roughy; groupers; Atlantic groundfish e.g. cod, etc; Atlantic sea haddock, pollack scallops; snapper
Monterey Bay Aquarium www.montereybayaquarium.org	Seafood Watch – a guide for consumers	Bluefin tuna; caviar (*Beluga & Caspian* sturgeon); Chilean seabass; Atlantic cod; ling; snapper; monkfish; orange roughy; roughy; sablefish; farmed salmon; Atlantic scallops; shrimp/prawns (all); swordfish
Australian Marine Conservation Society www.amcs.org.	Fish Forever	Orange roughy; ocean perch; aured fish; gemfish; scallop; rock ling; blue warehou; southern bluefin tuna; shark; blue eye; swordfish; marlin; giant crab; john dory; mirror dory; black bream
WWF www.wwf-uk.org	Fish of the Day	Deep-water species e.g. orange roughy; common skate
Marine Conservation Society www.mcsuk.org	Good Fish Guide	20 most vulnerable species (see Table 8)

Increasing the sustainability of the fish you eat

When deciding which fish to eat consider the following points. In particular consider the area and method of capture as a guide to the sustainability of the species and/or stock and the environmental impact of the method used to catch it.

What is it?

- What do you know about the life-history and biological characteristics of the species you are buying – what it is and how it lives?
- Are you aware of any specific issues associated with the species you intend to eat?
- Is it in season? (see Table 9) Does this coincide with the spawning period for that species?
- How big is it? Has it had a chance to mature and breed?
- Avoid eating known endangered or vulnerable species such as deep-water species, skate or shark (see Table 8).
- Diversify the type of fish you eat and so relieve demand for traditional or popular species such as cod and haddock etc.
- Choose whole fish. This will ensure that it is above the legal Minimum Landing Size (does not apply to farmed fish e.g. seabass is sold below the MLS of 36cm).
- Do not buy small fish or undersized fillets or portions of fish that fit the plate or appear to be from small or immature fish.
- Do not buy berried lobster or crab i.e. female animals carrying eggs
- Do not buy fish (caviar* or salted roe) or crustacean (coral) eggs or roe.

* farmed and vegetarian sources available.

Where is it caught?

- What do you know about the status of the stock or species in the area of capture - are numbers high or over-exploited?
- Is the species found locally in UK coastal waters?
- Is it caught and processed locally?
- Avoid purchasing fish from overfished or depleted stocks.
- Avoid products from countries or areas associated with poor management regimes.
- Choose organically farmed fish or fish from small-scale reputable producers.
- Examine the packaging to obtain information on country of origin and/or area of capture and any further information before making your purchase.

How is it caught?

- What do you know about how it is caught?
- What do you know about the issues associated with the method of capture?
- Is the fish labelled from accredited or approved sources?
- If you eat tuna buy only 'pole and line' caught tuna from approved sources.
- Where possible choose fish that have been caught by handline rather than in a large industrial trawl net.
- Avoid eating dredged scallops – diver caught scallops are generally larger and of better quality.
- Choose shellfish (e.g. Langoustines or scampi, prawns) that has been caught in a pot or trap rather than in set or trawl nets - pots are more selective and the catch generally of higher quality.

If in any doubt contact your supplier requesting more information on the area and method of capture. Ask your supplier or retailer for more in-store and labelling information. Be informed! Be sustainable!

Table 8: Top 20 species to be avoided as recommended by MCS

Species	Reason	Alternatives
Atlantic cod (from overfished stocks e.g. N Sea)	Species listed by IUCN	Line caught fish from Icelandic and Norwegian waters
Atlantic salmon	Wild stocks reduced by 50% in last 20 years	Responsibly and/or organically farmed salmon
Ling *Molva spp*	Deep-water species and habitat vulnerable to impacts of exploitation & trawling	None
Chilean Seabass (Patagonian toothfish)	Species threatened with extinction	None
Dogfish/Spurdog	Species listed by IUCN	None
European Hake	Species heavily over-fished and now scarce	South African hake (*M. capensis*)
Grouper	Many species are listed by IUCN	None
Haddock (from overfished stocks)	Species listed by IUCN	Line caught fish from Icelandic & Faroese waters
Marlin	Many species are listed by IUCN	None
Monkfish	Long-lived species vulnerable to exploitation. Mature females extremely rare	None
North Atlantic halibut	Species listed by IUCN	Line caught Greenland or Pacific species. Also farmed halibut
Orange roughy	Very long-lived species vulnerable to exploitation	None
European sea bass	Trawl fisheries target pre-spawning & spawning fish also high levels of cetacean by-catch	Line caught or farmed fish
Shark	Long-lived species vulnerable to exploitation	None
Skates & rays (*Rajidae*)	Long-lived species vulnerable to exploitation	None

Species	Reason	Alternatives
Snapper (*Lutjanus spp*)	Some species listed by IUCN, others over-exploited locally	None
Sturgeon	Long-lived species vulnerable to exploitation. 5 of the 6 Caspian Sea species listed by IUCN	None although this species is now farmed
Swordfish	Species listed by IUCN	None
Tuna	All commercially fished species listed by IUCN except skipjack & yellowfin which is over-fished	'Dolphin Friendly' (EII monitored) skipjack or yellowfin. Preferably pole & line caught.
Warm-water or tropical prawns	High by-catch levels and habitat destruction	Responsibly farmed prawns only

Spawning and season times

Fish are usually in peak condition prior to spawning and are described as 'spent' afterwards. For example, the fat content of oily fish such as herring is much lower in spring after spawning, than at other times of the year. Many fish aggregate to spawn and at this time are an easy target for fishermen's nets. Some species, such as the Pacific salmon and squid, die after spawning. For stocks to replenish themselves and for fishing to be sustainable, enough fish must be allowed to reproduce or spawn. Consumers can assist in the sustainable management of fisheries by demanding and purchasing only fish above or at the size at which it matures. This will ensure that the animal has spawned at least once in its lifetime. Also avoid eating fish which are targeted prior to spawning. For example, the fishery for seabass which takes place in winter in the Western Approaches off the south coast of England targets spawning and pre-spawning fish, as do fisheries for herring and orange roughy, which aggregate on seamounts to spawn.

Dover Sole

Catfish or Wolffish

Marlin

24

Table 9: In-season and spawning times for selected fish and shellfish species
(Sources: A Wheeler 1978 & Jackson et al 1995)

Common name	Spawning times*	In season
Brown crab	August - November	April - December
Cod	February - April	June - February
Haddock	February - June	May - February
Hake	March - August	June - March
Herring	March - November	May - December
Mackerel	May - August	All year
Plaice	January - March	May - February
Pollack	January - April	May - September
Scallop	April - September	September - March
Seabass	March - May	August - March
Skate (common)	February - August	May - February
Whiting	January - July (main spawning in spring)	June - February

* spawning times will vary for individual stocks, area and oceanographic conditions e.g. sea temperature

Octopus

Edible Crab

Baby fish don't spawn

In 1994 Boyd Line Management Services Ltd produced a paper warning of the dangers of buying small fillets of cod, haddock and plaice from baby fish -

Skate

'By favouring the buying of small fillets we are fuelling the forces which are rapidly destroying the stocks of these fish around the British Isles. Small fillets of these species, weighing less than 5 ounces, can only come from immature and juvenile fish, which have never spawned!'

Small fish are attractive to both processors and consumers because they are cheaper. The 110-140 g (4-5 oz) fillet is a good single meal sized portion and gives a better plate coverage than chunky pieces from larger fish. The surface area to weight ratio gives a greater potential to add a coating of cheaper material (e.g. breadcrumbs) than portions of similar weight cut from larger fish. Also portions cut from larger fish may not look like fish and as such are perceived as not being as attractive to consumers as smaller fish.

In response to dwindling stocks and capture of small fish, processors Young's Bluecrest Seafood Ltd have developed technology to shape and form larger fish into 'uniform' fish fillet shapes with good plate coverage. This process has enabled the company to meet customer and consumer demands and it has significant benefits for the fish as they can be allowed to grow to maturity.

Ling

Dogfish

Chapter Two
Labelling

Product labelling

What is environmental labelling?

As ethical and/or environmental awareness increases, consumers are demanding more information or guidance on the ethical or environmental performance of the products they purchase.

> 1 in 7 consumers identify ethical concerns (includes treatment of employees, environmental impacts, community support and company social and environmental policies) as a persuasive factor in purchasing decisions   (Source: ENDS 2001)

The concept of eco-labelling or environmental labelling was globally endorsed in 1992 at a meeting of the United Nations Committee on Environmental Development (UNCED). Governments agreed to encourage expansion of environmental labelling and other environmentally related product information programmes designed to assist consumers in making informed choices.

Why are products labelled?

Environmental labelling or 'eco-labelling' provides guidance for consumers to choose products and services that cause less damage to the environment and is defined by FAO as the:

'Voluntary granting of labels by a private or public body in order to inform consumers and thereby promote consumer products which are determined to be environmentally more friendly than other functionally and competitively similar products'.

Examples of ecolabels are Germany's 'Blue Angel', the first ecolabelling scheme introduced in the 1970s; the 'Nordic Swan' used in Norway, Finland, Denmark and Iceland, the entire lifecycle (cradle to grave) of the product has to be assessed in relation to the environment; the EU 'Flower' products must be environmentally sound throughout their lifecycle. The EU scheme is making slow progress, since all member states have to agree on the criteria for the many product categories concerned.

Eco-labelled products include batteries, detergents, clothing, building materials, compost, eggs, meat, vegetables, home appliances and paper products.

Food labelling

With increasing interest in and awareness of the nature and manner in which our food is produced, market-based instruments such as food labels are becoming more

widespread. In particular 'Organic' and 'Fair-trade' (see Chapter 9) labels or logos are becoming increasingly more popular, as demand for products that have been produced with regard for environmental and social issues increases.

Dab

Organic farming and food

The main principle of organic farming is that it severely restricts the use of artificial chemical fertilisers and pesticides and animals are reared without the routine use of drugs and antibiotics. It should be noted however that for meat classed as 'organic', animals are not necessarily free-ranging.

In Britain we currently import 75% of our organic food, of which 80% is organic fruit and vegetables. In a bid to increase the amount of organic production in Britain (only 3% of land in UK is organic compared to 10% in many northern European countries), a number of environmental organisations have joined forces to persuade the Government to back an Organic Targets Campaign. The Campaign is calling for an action plan for organic food and farming with 30% of agricultural land in England and Wales to be organic by 2010. The Secretariat for the Campaign is provided by Sustain – the alliance for better food and farming (see Appendix 1).

Organic labelling

All organic food production is governed by strict rules. Food sold as organic must originate from growers, processors and importers who are registered with an approved body and subject to regular inspection. More recently, organic standards have been developed for organically farmed fish and fishmeal (see Chapter 5).

UK Register of Organic Food Standards (UKROFS)

UKROFS, established in 1987, is responsible for ensuring that EC organic standards are properly applied in the UK by the various approved certifying authorities which register organic farms and processors. UKROF standards are the minimum standards which apply in the UK and are based on an EC Regulation ((EEC) No 2092/91).

Fish labelling

With the exception of 'dolphin-friendly' or 'dolphin-safe' labelling of canned tuna (see below), few marine products from wild caught fisheries are labelled to promote environmental responsibility. This is changing, however, as interest in accreditation of fisheries and labelling of fish products as a measure to harness consumer support for conserving fish stocks develops.

Marine labelling schemes

A number of organisations have developed or are developing labels to promote the quality and/or environmental credentials of wild-caught or farmed fish. These are summarised in Table 2.

Cockle

Table 2: Examples of marine labelling schemes available in the UK

Accrediting Body	Assured scheme	Logo	Products
Soil Association	Soil Association	Code: organic certification UK 5	Farmed fish, dairy foods, meat etc.
Marine Stewardship Council (MSC)	Marine Stewardship Council		Marine fish
Earth Island Institute (EII)	Dolphin Safe	See EII for details	Tuna
Scottish Quality Salmon (SQS)	Tartan Quality Mark		Farmed salmon
Frozen At Sea Fillets (FASF)	Ocean Wild Mark		Frozen fish

Soil Association

The Soil Association (SA) was founded in 1946 and is one of about 12 certifying bodies regulated by UKROFS. It undertakes more than 70% of all certification in the UK and is the most widely recognised organic logo in Britain.

Marine Stewardship Council

In 1997 the international conservation organisation WWF and Unilever, the world's largest buyer of frozen food, formed a conservation partnership to create economic incentives for sustainable fishing by establishing the Marine Stewardship Council (MSC). MSC has been an independent, international, non-profit making body with charitable status since 1999. Following a two year consultation period with various organisations around the world it has established a set of Principles and Criteria for Sustainable Fishing which are based on the 1995 FAO Code of Conduct for Responsible Fishing. The set of Principles and Criteria are the standard against which fisheries certifications may take place (see Appendix 2). Fisheries meeting these standards will be eligible for third party certification by independent certifying bodies accredited by MSC. Products from certified fisheries will then be able to carry an on-pack logo allowing consumers to select seafood products they know come from sustainable, well-managed sources. Fisheries certified by MSC to date are summarised in Table 3. There are also about 20-30 other fisheries world-wide at various stages of the certification process.

The MSC has support from over 100 organisations in over 20 countries. Organisations include key retailers, processors, conservation groups and governments. Many of the main UK supermarket chains and retailers are signatories to the MSC initiative and are actively involved in its development. Sainsburys became the first UK food retailer to sell MSC labelled products. Multi-national Unilever, owner of the Bird's Eye brand, has pledged to source all of its fish from sustainable fisheries by 2005. New Zealand hoki, the first white fish labelled to the MSC standard, is one of a new range of products launched by Young's Bluecrest last year called 'Fish for Life'. The product will carry the strapline 'Good for Me, Good for the Sea' highlighting its focus on species from sustainable sources.

Table 3: Summary of fisheries certified by MSC up to December 2001

Fishery	Species	Date certified
UK Thames Blackwater	Herring	March 2000
Western Australia	Rock Lobster	March 2000
Alaska	Salmon	September 2000
New Zealand	Hoki	March 2001
Burry Inlet, Wales	Cockles	April 2001
South West Handline Fishery, Cornwall	Mackerel	September 2001

Dolphin safe labelling
'Dolphin safe' labelling was established in the USA – the largest consumer of tuna in the world, in 1990 with the aim of reducing the number of dolphin deaths in tuna fisheries in the Eastern Tropical Pacific (ETP).

The main problem with by-catch of dolphins was first identified in the ETP in the 1950s, where schools of yellowfin tuna swim in association with dolphin and where one third of the world's harvest of yellowfin tuna, representing a quarter of the world's tuna catch, is taken. Today the number of yellowfin tuna taken in nets set deliberately on dolphins only accounts for a very small proportion (3.3% in 1997) of tuna on the world market.

'Dolphin-safe' labelling was developed to assure consumers that the tuna they purchase is caught using methods that do not involve the deliberate hunting, capture and subsequent death of dolphins.

Earth Island Institute
The Earth Island Institute (EII) was founded in 1982 in San Francisco, California by veteran environmentalist David Brower (who died in 2000). Since its inception, more than 50 projects have been launched, including its International Marine Mammal Project, to stop the slaughter of dolphins and whales. In 1988, EII was responsible for organising the most successful consumer-led boycott of a product, tuna - resulting in tuna companies adopting 'dolphin-safe' standards in 1990 and the requirement that all US tuna be 'dolphin-safe'. In 2000 the Clinton Administration lifted the US embargo

on 'dolphin-deadly' (see below) tuna. However, since such tuna cannot use the 'dolphin-safe' label, to date little has appeared on the US market. If this situation changes EII has vowed to lead another boycott of such products.

The most reputable and stringent standards for 'dolphin-safe' labelling are those developed by the EII. These standards were developed in 1990 by EII and the HJ Heinz Corporation (the largest supplier of canned tuna in the world) and have been adopted by approximately 300 tuna companies, canneries, brokers, import associations, retail stores and restaurant chains around the globe.

EII 'dolphin-safe' criteria prohibits intentional chasing, encircling or netting of marine mammals and use of driftnets and gill-nets. EII 'dolphin-safe' criteria also prohibits any accidental killing or serious injury of dolphins, which is rare outside of dolphin net sets, but does sometimes occur. The organisation also works to reduce by-catch of other non-target species (sea turtles, sharks, marine mammals and birds etc.) and juvenile tunas.

All companies, participating in the EII project, representing more than 90% of the world's canned tuna markets and including the US, Canada and Europe, are required to sign an EII policy document pertinent to the section of the industry the company represents (i.e. fishing, processing or distributing) and must comply with the following restrictions and conditions in order for the tuna to be certified as 'dolphin-safe':

- The use of driftnets is prohibited.
- Intentionally encircling or 'setting' purse-seine nets on marine mammals (known as dolphin-fishing) at sea is prohibited.
- Shipments of tuna taken by purse-seine nets in the Eastern Tropical Pacific are required to be accompanied by documentation which certifies that an observer was on board the fishing vessel (400 gross tons and above only) during the entire trip and that purse-seine nets were not intentionally deployed during the trip to encircle marine mammals.
- Companies must permit EII monitors to observe fishing operations or carry out any inspections deemed necessary by EII.
- Companies are required to make a sincere effort to reduce by-catch in their fishing operations by utilizing methods such as larger mesh sizes and release of non target species while still alive.
- Long-line vessels are required to incorporate effective devices to safely discourage sea birds from approaching baited hooks.
- Crew members are required to avoid causing death or injury to marine mammals and other non-target species by, but not limited to, deploying nets only after dolphins have been driven away unharmed from the fishing area and/or carefully releasing animals, alive and not injured when possible, which may wander into fishing nets.
- Crew members are prohibited from shooting, harpooning or in any way intentionally harming marine mammals or using their flesh for bait.
- Participation in shark-finning operations is prohibited.
- Companies and their subsidiaries or affiliates must not be involved in whaling operations, dolphin drive fisheries or shark fin fisheries.

Earth Island Institute's International Monitoring Programme
EII's International Monitoring Programme (IMP) was established in 1990 to monitor all aspects of the international tuna industry to ensure that companies are not selling tuna caught by setting nets on dolphins, or in drift nets. Monitors are located in every continent of the world including Europe.

IMP Europe was set up in 1992 in Milan, Itlay. Tuna operations and sales are monitored in Portugal (Azores), Spain, France, UK, Sweden, Norway, Belgium, Germany, Austria, Switzerland, Italy and Turkey. Companies participating in IMP Europe include major retail chains, brokers and importers and comprise 90% of the European tuna industry. IMP Europe also networks with EII and IMP monitors in Thailand, Mexico, Philippines, Colombia, Costa Rica, Panama, Venezuela, Indonesia, Seychelles, Mauritius, Senegal, the Ivory Coast and the EII HQ in Hawaii and San Francisco, USA to check tuna shipments.
More than 7 million dolphins have drowned in tuna nets in the Eastern Tropical Pacific (ETP) in the past 40 years. Since 1990 the IMP, together with the support and collaboration of the tuna industry, has managed to reduce dolphin mortality in the region by 98%, from approximately 80-100,000 dolphin kills per year in the 1980's to current levels of 2-3,000 animals per year. It is important to note that these are reported kills and it is likely that many more dolphins are dying in net sets than are being reported, because dolphin populations are not recovering.

Dolphin-deadly
Standards for dolphin-safe tuna have also been developed by the Inter-American Tropical Tuna Commission (IATCC, see Chapter 6) and the Agreement on the International Dolphin Conservation Program (AIDCAP). AIDCAP is a binding international instrument adopted in 1998 by countries (including Mexico, Venezuela, USA, Spain and Ecuador) fishing for tuna in the ETP. Parties to the Agreement are required to adhere to certain management measures to progressively reduce dolphin mortality in their fishing operations. Enforcement of these measures, however, is left entirely to the discretion of the individual national fisheries agencies and violations are often ignored. Although a 'binding' agreement, nations can leave at any time – Mexico is currently threatening to leave the Agreement because they cannot falsely label their tuna as 'dolphin-safe' and sell it in the USA. The IATCC/AIDCAP standards are weaker than those international standards approved by EII and do not prohibit the intentional chasing, netting or encirclement of dolphins (known as 'dolphin fishing' which is 'dolphin-deadly'). Provided there is no observed mortality or injury to dolphins by onboard IATCC observers, the tuna can be labelled as 'dolphin-safe'. This definition is misleading as many unobserved deaths are caused by physiological stress (some dolphin schools are chased and netted as often as three times a day), injuries incurred during netting with subsequent death after release and death of calves who become separated from their mothers. Furthermore, the IATCC definition allows mixing of 'dolphin-safe' and 'dolphin-deadly' tuna aboard ship!

UK Retailers and dolphin-safe
Although EII does not yet have a uniform 'dolphin-safe' logo they are in the process of adopting one for introduction to the European market in the next few years. In the past companies adhering to the EII Standards produced their own 'dolphin-safe' label. Unfortunately, this system has become confusing (particularly in the US) due to the introduction of the IATCC 'dolphin-deadly' labelling standards. For example, several of the Mexican companies that continue to kill dolphins label all of their tuna as 'Amigo de Delfin' (dolphin-friendly). Although little of the 'dolphin-deadly' tuna is likely to enter the European market it is on sale in Spain and EII is working to address this situation. To ensure that tuna is in fact 'dolphin-friendly', UK consumers should only buy brands produced by an EII listed and approved company.

Details of main brand name tuna on sale in UK supermarkets is presented in Table 4. Many of the supermarket chains have policy statements on sourcing and buying tuna. These may be written as single-issue statements or incorporated in a wider environmental policy document.

Table 4: Method and area of capture for tinned and fresh tuna products sold in UK Supermarkets*

Brand name	Area of capture	Location of fresh or cannery operations	Tuna species canned (c) and or fresh (f)	Fishing methods	Label details (canned only)	Environmental Policy and/or Policy Statement for single issues
Waitrose	Indian and Pacific Oceans	Seychelles, Sri Lanka, Ecuador, Reunion Is., Thailand & Philippines	Yellowfin (c) & (f) Skipjack (c)	Long-line	Caught using fishing methods which do not harm dolphins or other marine mammals	Technical policy; statement for tuna; EII monitored
John West	Indian, Atlantic & Western Pacific	Ghana and Seychelles	Skipjack (c) Yellowfin (c) (not from ETP)	Purse seine in Atlantic, Indian & W Pacific. Also pole and line off Ghana.	Dolphin friendly	Policy statement for tuna; EII monitored
Glenryck	Indian, Atlantic & Western Pacific	Ghana, Peru and Thailand	Skipjack (c) Yellowfin (c)	Purse seine	Dolphin friendly	EII monitored
Safeway	Indian, Atlantic & Western Pacific	Sri Lanka & Indonesia (f); Thailand, Seychelles, Ivory Coast, Senegal, Spain & Colombia	Skipjack (c) Yellowfin (f) & (c)	Purse seine (c) & Long-line and pole and line (f)	Caught in a manner which minimises risk to marine mammals (currently under review)	Canned tuna is EII monitored Fresh tuna subject of general welfare statement.
Somerfield	Indian Ocean	Maldives and Indonesia	Any tuna (thunnus) species (f); Skipjack (c)	Long-line	Dolphin friendly	None at this time. Member of EII.
Marks & Spencer	Pacific and Indian Oceans	Seychelles, Sri Lanka, Ecuador, Reunion Is., Thailand & Philippines.	Skipjack (c) Big Eye (f) Yellowfin (f)	Purse seine Long-line Long-line	Dolphin friendly	Environmental Policy; EII monitored
Tesco	Atlantic, Pacific & Indian Ocean	Thailand, Philippines, Ghana, Seychelles, Mauritius, Maldives, Spain & Ecuador	Yellowfin (c) Skipjack (c)	Purse seine; long-line; pole & line	Dolphin friendly	Policy statement for tuna; Fresh & canned tuna all EII monitored

* all major retailers were invited to provide information for the compilation of this table. The information in this table is complied from responses received.

Although some countries such as Mexico, Venezuela and some boats from Panama and Colombia continue to deliberately net dolphins in their tuna operations, the Maldives is an example of a tuna fishing nation which uses traditional pole and line methods to capture tuna. In waters around the Maldives all marine mammals and turtles are protected and net-fishing is banned within 200 miles of their coastline.

Tuna

Traditional methods of capturing tuna (pole and line) are not associated with high by-catch levels of marine mammals, turtles and birds. They are also more labour intensive providing employment and income for artisanal fishermen (see Chapter 9).

Scottish Quality Salmon

All members of Scottish Quality Salmon (SQS) (formally the Scottish Salmon Growers Association) must participate in independently operated Product Certification Schemes operated by Food Certification (Scotland) (FCS) Ltd. FCS is accredited by United Kingdom Accreditation Service (UKAS) to operate such Schemes and is also registered as an organic sector body by UKROFS. Participation in the Certification Scheme entitles SQS members to use the Tartan Quality Mark (TQM) in the UK. Every salmon carrying the TQM can be traced back to source through a unique number printed on the gill tag on whole salmon or labels on pre-packed fresh salmon portions. In addition to participation in the Product Certification Scheme all SQS members are required to sign up to a Sustainable Development Strategy (see Chapter 5). SQS is dedicated to improving the quality and sustainability of salmon farming in Scotland and the growing membership now represents around 65% of the tonnage produced by the Scottish salmon farming industry.

Frozen At Sea Fillets Association

The Frozen at Sea Fillets Association (FASFA) was established in 1990 to communicate the benefits of frozen-at-sea fillets of fish to the trade and consumer; establish quality standards for frozen fish; and ensure that environmental standards are observed to ensure a sustainable, long-term supply of fish. FASFA members (which includes companies such as Young's Bluecrest) fish for cod, haddock and saithe in the waters around Iceland and in the Barents Sea. These waters are strictly managed by the Icelandic and Norwegian authorities with the objective of providing a sustainable harvest. Iceland operates a

Flounder

strict harvesting regime with quotas designed to ensure that no more than 25% of the spawning stock biomass (SSB) is removed. Minimum Landing Sizes (MLSs) and mesh sizes are also much larger than those currently adhered to in waters administered by the Common Fisheries Policy (CFP). Discarding is also prohibited in these waters.

Grey Mullet

FASFA is introducing an 'Ocean Wild' Quality Mark which will be applied to the packaging of fish produced by member vessels which meet certain standards. The standards were set with the objective of being able to assure the customer and consumer that the management regimes of the fisheries where the vessels operate is of the highest order and that the standards of production on board the vessels and distribution and storage criteria are of the optimum quality.

Labelling for origin and species

Labelling and product information for fish and its products varies according to the nature of the product – fresh, frozen or tinned – and the retailer or processor. Fresh fish tends to be accompanied by the least information whilst for tinned or processed fish, the country of origin is usually stated. Information on the method of capture is generally absent.

From January 2002 labelling for origin and species became mandatory in the EC for fish (whole and fillets only – legislation does not apply to further processed products e.g. fish fingers etc.) which will have to be labelled with the following information:

- The commercial name of the species (addition of the scientific name is discretional).
- Production methods i.e. caught at sea or in fresh water, farmed or cultivated.
- Area where the fish was caught.

No information relating to the method of capture is as yet required. The Marine Conservation Society is working to encourage producers or manufacturers and retailers to provide more comprehensive labelling, including details on area and method of capture, in order that consumers can make more informed choices about the fish they buy.

It should be noted that information on origin on the packaging of processed fish e.g. fillets in breadcrumbs, relates to the origin of the product and not to the origin of the raw material i.e. the fish (unless otherwise stated).

Chapter Three
Species Tables

How to use the A-Z Species Tables

Use the index to find the species you are interested in. From the information given for each species in the table, particularly that given for its status and method of capture, determine the environmental and ethical sustainability of the species you intend to eat. Refer to the chapters indicated in the relevant section of the table for further information.

Avoid eating fish which are:

Listed as Critically Endangered, Endangered, Vulnerable or at Lower Risk by IUCN (see details on species or stock status)

or

From stocks outside safe biological limits or stocks being fished at levels which are too high (see details on species or stock status)

Caught using methods which involve excessive by-catch of non-target species (see fishery and marine ecosystem related issues)

Caught using methods which cause damage to the seabed e.g. dredging (see fishery and marine ecosystem related issues)

The 20 least eco-friendly species are summarised in Table 8 (Chapter 1).

To increase the sustainability of the fish you eat (see Chapter 1) choose fish which is:

Sustainably managed or from stocks within safe biological limits

Caught using selective methods which do not involve by-catch of non-target species e.g. handlines, pots or traps

Caught using methods which minimise damage to the seabed e.g. diver caught rather than dredged scallops

Gurnard

Species Name

Common and scientific names	Most common name/s for the species (latin or scientific name in italics in brackets)
Species detail	Details of the life-history and biology of species. In particular the size of the fish at maturity and time of spawning. Consumers are encouraged to seek out and buy mature sized wild-caught fish. Farmed species are often immature when harvested.
Species distribution	Indication of the distribution of the species i.e. where it is found. Information on distribution of stocks where applicable.
Species and/ or stock status	Indication of the status of the species and its vulnerability to overfishing. Information on the status of individual stocks where available from ICES assessments.
Method of capture Chapter 4 & 8	The way in which the species is caught. Fishing methods are described in detail in Chapter 4. The likely impacts associated with individual methods are described in Chapters 4 and 8.
Management Chapter 6	Details of management framework i.e. European Union Common Fisheries Policy (CFP) and/or Regional Fisheries Organisation (RFO). Also details of Technical Conservation Measures i.e. whether the species is subject to quota restrictions, minimum landing size restrictions or whether the species is non-pressure stock i.e. no management restrictions in place. See Chapter 6 for detail.
Fishery and marine ecosystem related issues Chapter 5 & 8	Details of specific fishery and marine ecosystem related issues such as stock collapse; habitat destruction; by-catch of marine birds . See Chapter 8 for detail. Issues related to fish farming are detailed in Chapter 5.
Health, welfare and socio-economic related issues Chapter 7 & 9	Details of issues associated with human health, welfare and socio-economic issues such as food-miles and unsustainable production . See Chapters 7 and 9 for detail.
Product details Chapter 1 & 2	Details of product including other uses where known and details of labelled products where available. See Chapters 1 and 2 for detail.
Season Chapter 1	These are the months in which the fish is in condition for eating (NB these are not the only months that the species is available to consumers as many are available fresh and/or frozen all year round). Compare these times with the times at which the species is known to spawn, given in the section on Species details, and avoid buying fish which has been caught during or before their spawning time.

Species Index A-Z

Anchovy

Common and scientific names	Anchovy or European anchovy (*Engrualis encrasicolus*)
Species detail	The only European member of the Engraulidae family. A relative of the herring, it is a small schooling fish feeding on plankton. In summer anchovy move inshore to spawn in June to August. In winter it moves into deeper waters. Maximum length 20cm. More usually between 9 and 12 cm.
Species distribution	Members of the family are found world-wide in temperate and tropical seas and are the basis of commercially important fisheries. Main Atlantic stocks in Bay of Biscay and off Portuguese coast. Also Mediterranean, Black and Aegean Seas.
Species and/ or stock status	Bay of Biscay stock close to collapse due to overfishing and poor recruitment. ICES has recommended that the fishery be closed.
Method of capture	Purse seine.
Management	Managed by TAC and MLS (10cms in Portuguese waters; 12 cms in other areas) in EU waters. TAC divided amongst Spain (80%), Portugal (12%) and France (8%).
Fishery and marine ecosystem related issues	Removal of huge quantities of small plankton feeding fish at the base of the food chain; by-catch of marine mammals; anchovy (*Engraulis ringens*) targeted by industrial fisheries for reduction purposes (fish meal & fertilizer) in Peru; small anchovies used as livebait in Spanish tuna fisheries.
Health, welfare and socio-economic related issues	Overfishing of Peruvian anchovy has led to a decrease in numbers of guano (sea bird manure) producing birds and the amount of guano available to be made into fertilizer.
Product details	Fresh; salted; marinated; canned or bottled (in oil); anchovy paste. Widely used in Mediterranean cooking. Also popular as pizza topping. E. ringens are the basis for commercially important industrial fisheries and are an important source of animal feed and, indirectly, of fertilizer.
Season	June - December

Blue ling

Common and scientific names	Blue ling *(Molva dypterygia)*
Species detail	A member of the cod family. It is a deep-water species living in much deeper water (350 –500 m) than its relative the ling *(Molva molva)*. In common with most deep-water species it is slow growing, taking 5-6 years to reach sexual maturity. Length at first maturity is 74 cm for males and 89 cm for females. It is a long slender bodied fish. Attains a maximum length of 1.5 m and is known to live up to 20-30 years. Spawning takes place in deep water in April to May. Little is known of the early life history of this species.
Species distribution	Found in waters in the north-east and north-west Atlantic; in deep water west of the British Isles, Iceland, Faroes and Greenland. Also found in the Mediterranean. Major commercial stock in the North Atlantic.
Species and/ or stock status	Assessment of deep-water resources in the North Atlantic indicate that in many areas the species is outside safe biological limits and the stock is close to collapse.
Method of capture	Long-line and trawl.
Management	The North-East Atlantic Fisheries Commission (NEAFC) has responsibility for the management of this species in the north-east Atlantic in international waters. It is an unregulated resource under the NEAFC Convention i.e. there are no limits on how many fish may be taken. It is managed by quota in national waters of Iceland and Norway. MLS of 70 cm specified in EU waters.
Fishery and marine ecosystem related issues	A deep-water species vulnerable to overfishing because of its life-history characteristics – slow growth, longevity and age of sexual maturity; blue ling is taken in mixed, demersal type fisheries associated with by-catch and discarding of non-targeted species. Very little is known about the impacts of trawling on the sea-bed in the deep-water environment.
Health, welfare and socio-economic related issues	No specific issues.
Product details	Marketed fresh and salted. Available in UK but more common in France.
Season	No information

Bream

Common and scientific names	Black bream or sea bream *(Spondyliosoma cantharus)*. 8 species of sea bream have been reported in northern European seas but only 2 are common – black and red or blackspot seabream *(Pagellus bogaraveo)*. Only black bream is described here.
Species detail	Black bream are demersal spawners and lay their eggs in hollows or nests in the gravel of the seabed. Spawning occurs in April and May in the English Channel in inshore waters. Juveniles do not move far from the nest area and remain in inshore waters for 2-3 years. In winter, adult bream move offshore into deeper water. Black bream all mature as females at a length of around 20 cm and remain female to a length of about 30 cm. However, once bream exceed 30 cm, they may change into males and all bream over 40 cm in length are males. This may have important consequences for the sustained reproductive capacity of a bream stock, given that egg survival may be enhanced by the larger males guarding nests.
Species distribution	Black bream are distributed in north-east shelf waters from Norway and the Orkney Islands south to the Mediterranean Sea and the Canary Islands. They are not present in the Baltic and are most abundant in the Channel and south to the Mediterranean Sea.
Species and/ or stock status	There is no assessment of black bream stocks, but there is no evidence that the fishery in the Channel is unsustainable. Channel stocks were heavily fished in the 1970s and 80s but have recovered somewhat in recent years.
Method of capture	Trawl and fixed nets. Also taken by anglers using rod and line.
Management	No specific management arrangements for this species – non-pressure stock.
Fishery and marine ecosystem related issues	No specific issues
Health, welfare and socio-economic related issues	No specific issues
Product details	Sea bream are sold whole, usually gutted, and need to be descaled before cooking. Bream may be grilled, fried, barbecued or baked.
Season	Black sea bream July – December; gilthead *(Sparus auratus)* sea bream is widely farmed in the Mediterranean and is available all year.

Brill

Common and scientific names	Brill (*Scophthalamus rhombus*)
Species detail	Brill belongs to a small family of flatfish (*Scophthalmidae*) which have both eyes on the left side of the head. Family comprises several species which includes megrim and turbot. Brill lives on sandy or mixed sea bottoms. Able to change colour of the eyed side, matching the bottom they rest on. It attains a maximum length of 75 cm, usually 50 cm. Weight up to 8 kgs. Maximum reported age 6 years. Spawns in spring and summer.
Species distribution	North-east Atlantic: Mediterranean and Black Sea; eastern Atlantic along European coasts from Morocco to 64° North. Brill reaches the northern extremity of its range in northern Europe; north of England and Denmark its abundance declines quickly.
Species and/ or stock status	No specific information available, but, like turbot remains a relatively scarce species in many areas.
Method of capture	Hook and line; by-catch in trawl nets; set nets.
Management	Brill is included in the TAC for turbot in EU waters of North Sea- no distinction is apparently made between these two species. No MLS specified.
Fishery and marine ecosystem related issues	No specific issues
Health, welfare and socio-economic related issues	No specific issues
Product details	Less tasty than turbot, brill is of some commercial importance. Sold fresh and frozen. Eaten steamed, fried, boiled, broiled, baked etc. May be sold whole but usually in steaks or fillets.
Season	June - February

Brown Crab

Common and scientific names	Brown or edible crab (*Cancer pagurus*)
Species detail	The brown crab is the heaviest British crab and is found on the lower shore down to about 100m, usually amongst rocks or under boulders. Typical carapace width up to 15cm sometimes 25cm across. It has 5 pairs of legs including one pair of large black-tipped pincers and a characteristic 'pie-crust' edge to its shell. Periodically crabs shed their shells to grow. Crabs mate just after the female has shed her shell, when the carapace is soft. Brown crabs spawn mainly in the winter months. Most male or 'cock' crabs over 11 cm are sexually mature, at this size they are about 3 years old. Females or 'hens' mature at about 13-15 cm depending on area. The number of eggs carried by the female crab is related to carapace width and may vary from 1 to 3 million eggs. Females carrying eggs are termed 'berried' females.
Species distribution	A widely distributed crustacean in coastal waters of the Mediterranean, Atlantic, English Channel and North Sea. Widely distributed around the UK coast.
Species and/ or stock status	Many stocks are now overfished due to high fishing pressure. It has been estimated that more than 60% of our crab populations are being harvested each year reducing spawning stocks to well below 25% of their unfished level. Important fisheries for crab occur off the Devon and Norfolk (Cromer crab) coasts.
Method of capture	Crab pots or creels. Also taken as by-catch in net and trawl fisheries.
Management	MLS varies throughout the UK e.g. Devon and Cornwall 140mm for hens and 160mm for cocks. North Sea 115mm for both. Some EU landing sizes are less strict than existing national legislation. A proposal to introduce a restrictive licensing scheme for shellfish is under consideration for UK waters. In England and Wales Sea Fisheries Committees manage shellfisheries through their local byelaws.
Fishery and marine ecosystem related issues	Overfishing – fishing effort is increasing so that edible crab is at risk of being exploited beyond sustainable limits; landings are generally dominated by smaller animals just above the legal MLS; removal of large breeding females from stock. Do not buy or eat 'berried' or egg bearing females, it is illegal and damages stocks.
Health, welfare and socio-economic related issues	Crabs may be killed by 'drowning' in fresh water. This can take up to 5 hours depending on water temperature. A quicker and more humane method – provided it is carried out expertly - is to 'spike' it in its two nerve centres – behind the eyes and on the underside of the 'apron' (the small flap on the underside of the carapace or shell). Crabs are not boiled alive (un-like lobster) because they shed their claws and their meat deteriorates.
Product details	Eaten cooked and dressed whole; crab meat – brown meat is found in the body shell and white meat in the claws and legs; crab sticks; crab paste.
Season	April – December

Catfish

Common and scientific names	Catfish or wolffish. Also known as rockfish *(Anarhichas lupus)*
Species detail	Catfish belongs to the family of wolf fishes *Anarhichidae* and is related to the blennies. The catfish is one of three species found in northern European seas. It is easily identified by its large head and strong teeth ideally suited to crushing crustaceans (crab & sea urchin) and molluscs (mussels, whelks etc.) upon which it feeds. They are solitary animals and live close to the seabed in depths of 60-300 m in British waters. They can grow to 125 - 150 cm although the majority of animals landed are less than 100 cm. Catfish spawn in winter.
Species distribution	Species confined to temperate and boreal waters of Northern hemisphere and distributed throughout north-eastern and north-western Atlantic. Also occurs in the North Sea.
Species and/ or stock status	No specific information available.
Method of capture	Taken as by-catch in mixed trawl fisheries around the UK coast.
Management	No specific management regime. Non-quota or non-pressure stock species.
Fishery and marine ecosystem	It is a slow growing fish and would quickly be affected by heavy fishing.
Health, welfare and socio-economic related issues	No specific issues
Product details	Eaten fresh - its flesh is well flavoured and firm. May be baked, grilled or fried. Skin can be used for leather. Most of the UK catch is exported to the Continent.
Season	February - July

Chilean Seabass

Common and scientific names	Chilean seabass; seabass; Antarctic seabass; Patagonian toothfish or icefish (*Dissostichus eleginoides*).
Species detail	Chilean seabass is a deep-water species and lives in depths from 300 to 3,500m. It is a slow-growing fish and does not breed until it is 10-12 years. At this stage it is about 70 cm long. It can reach ages of 50 years and a maximum length of 220 cm. They spawn from June to September. Natural predators are sperm whale and elephant seal.
Species distribution	It is found throughout large areas of the sub-Antarctic oceans, South Pacific, Atlantic and Indian oceans. Major stocks in Southern Ocean, South Atlantic and South Pacific. Also found around seamounts of the Indian Ocean and continental shelves of most sub-Antarctic islands.
Species and/ or stock status	Species threatened by illegal fishing. Since the beginning of the fishery in the mid-1990s, stocks have been driven to the brink of collapse. Commercial extinction is expected within the next 2-3 years.
Method of capture	Long-lines, several miles long with thousands of baited hooks; and bottom trawl.
Management	Management falls under the jurisdiction of both state and inter-governmental agencies. Species fished in EEZ's or national waters of countries such as Chile and Argentina. Marine resources managed by CCAMLR in the Southern Ocean. TAC agreed by members.
Fishery and marine ecosystem related issues	Overfishing by 'pirate' fishermen. IUU threatens species with extinction; in excess of 68,000 seabirds (albatross & petrels) die on long-lines in the illegal fishery alone - populations of wandering albatross are declining at an estimated 1% per year due to these fisheries; Chilean seabass play an important part in the ecosystem of the Southern Ocean.
Health, welfare and socio-economic related issues	Illegal or pirate fishing.
Product details	Marketed: fresh, whole or in steaks or fillets, and frozen. Eaten: fresh, grilled, poached, sautéed and smoked.
Season	Available all year

Clam

Common and scientific names	Clam. Various species available in the UK: the carpet shell (*Venerupis pullastra*), surf clams or trough shells (*Spisula solidissima*), warty venus (*Venus verrucosa*), razor clam (*Enis spp. & Pharus legumen*), donax clams (*Donax spp.*), hard shell clam (*Callista chione*) and the Manila or short-necked clam or Ribbed carpet shell (*Ruditapes or Tapes philippinarum*).
Species detail	Clams are bivalve molluscs. They have symmetrical shells and a mouth but no head. Clams characteristically lie buried from just beneath the surface to depths of about 0.5 m. Clams draw in and expel water for respiration and feeding through two tubes or siphons. They usually live on sandy or muddy bottoms. Clams are sedentary and rarely travel over the bottom as do other bivalves. Eggs are usually shed by the female into the water and fertilised there by sperm released from the male. Eggs develop into larvae that swim briefly before settling permanently on the bottom.
Species distribution	All species are widely distributed in inter-tidal waters throughout UK and temperate waters.
Species and/ or stock status	No specific information available. Stocks vulnerable to local over-exploitation and depletion. (Giant clams *(Tridacuids spp.)* found only in tropical waters are protected by CITES. Numbers have been greatly reduced by heavy exploitation for human consumption and the aquarium trade).
Method of capture	Dredging (including suction or hydraulic dredging); hand-picking or collection. Traditional methods of harvesting molluscs involve the use of hand tools such as tongs and rakes. Species such as Manila clam and American hard shell or quahog clam *(Mercenaria mercenaria)* are commercially farmed.
Management	In UK may be managed under Regulating or Several Orders (see Chapter 5) in coastal waters. Also under Sea Fishery byelaws. Statutory Agencies also have an interest in the management of bivalve molluscs. EU MLS specified for most species.
Fishery and marine ecosystem related issues	Removal of prey species for birds and other marine life; disturbance of seabed or substrate – suction dredging reduces number of invertebrate species by more than 90%.
Health, welfare and socio-economic related issues	Clams are filter feeders and can accumulate toxins in their flesh. However water quality standards for shellfish (bivalve & gastropod molluscs) for human consumption is controlled and may only be harvested commercially from designated shellfish growing areas.
Product details	Eaten cooked fresh in clam chowder. Also cooked and marinated or used in soup.
Season	Bivalves in season when there is a 'R' in the month. Farmed species available all year.

Cockle

Common and scientific names	Cockle (*Cerastoderma edule*)
Species detail	The common cockle is a bivalve mollusc. It has two identical oval shells or valves scored with radiating ridges. Shell size up to 5 cm long. The inner surface is shiny and white. It is found buried in mud and sand in estuaries and on beaches. An organ called a siphon allows the animal to feed and breathe whilst buried in the sand itself. Spawns in May to August.
Species distribution	It is distributed widely on coastlines of Mediterranean, Atlantic, English Channel and the North Sea. Nearly all commercial concentrations of edible or common cockle occur on large intertidal flats in lower reaches of estuaries.
Species and/ or stock status	Stocks vulnerable to local over-exploitation and depletion. Cockle populations are most vulnerable from Easter to the end of Summer, when they breed, releasing larvae, which settle into the sand and grow.
Method of capture	Dredging (including suction or hydraulic dredging); tractor-towed harvesters; hand-picking or collection. Traditional methods of harvesting molluscs involve the use of hand tools such as tongs and rakes, and may be the only methods allowed in some areas. Burry Inlet (SW Wales) cockle fishery is certified as an environmentally responsible fishery by the Marine Stewardship Council.
Management	Managed under Regulating or Several Orders (see Chapter 5) in coastal waters of England and Wales. Also under Sea Fishery Committee and Local Authority byelaws. Statutory Agencies also have an interest in the management of molluscs e.g. introduction of size limits.
Fishery and marine ecosystem related issues	Overexploitation by commercial or mechanised harvesting – decreasing numbers and sizes at some beaches and estuaries; harvesting affects burrowing behaviour of cockles; removal of prey species for birds and other marine life; disturbance of seabed or mud and sand on beaches and in estuaries.
Health, welfare and socio-economic related issues	Cockles and filter feeders can accumulate toxins in their flesh. However water quality standards for shellfish (bivalve & gastropod molluscs) for human consumption is controlled and may only be harvested commercially from designated shellfish growing areas.
Product details	Eaten fresh and cooked in shell. Also used as bait by anglers. MSC labelled cockles available.
Season	Bivalves in season when there is a 'R' in the month.

Cod

Common and scientific names	Cod; Atlantic cod; Northern cod *(Gadus morhua)*.
Species detail	Cod is a cold-temperate (boreal), demersal species. It belongs to the family of fish known as gadoids. Cod spawn in winter and spring in February to April. In the North Sea, cod reach maturity at 4-5 years old at a length of approximately 50 cm. Prefers shallow waters over the continental shelf down to a depth of about 600 m. Cod produce millions of eggs and can live to 60 years old.
Species distribution	Distributed throughout the northern hemisphere in the east and west Atlantic. However, cod exist as a number of discrete or isolated populations or stocks. Important stocks are: North Sea; north-east Arctic; Greenland; Iceland; Faroe Islands; Skaggerak & Kattegat; Irish Sea; Newfoundland; Labrador; and Grand Banks.
Species and/ or stock status	The best known species of cod in Britain is *Gadus morhua*, the Atlantic cod. Due to decades of relentless overfishing many commercial stocks are now close to collapse. Atlantic cod is assessed as Vulnerable by IUCN. North Sea stock on brink of collapse - 40-45% of 2-8 year old fish removed every year by fishing. However, only one fifth of the cod consumed in Britain is taken from this area. The remaining four fifths of cod eaten in Britain come from the waters of the Barents Sea, and the seas around Iceland and Norway. All stocks except Icelandic stock are outside safe biological limits. Although biomass for Icelandic stock is overestimated and limited quota cuts have been introduced. Despite recovery plan for Irish Sea stock, which is outside safe limits, the TAC was increased by nearly 50% for 2002!
Method of capture	Cod largely targeted by otter trawls and gillnets in the North Sea. Other methods are hook and line and longline. Also taken by anglers. Cod is now farmed in Norway and Scotland.
Management	Species managed through a system of TACs and quotas and technical measures in EU waters. MLS of 35 cms (30 cms in Skaggerak & Kattegat). Cod recovery plans recently introduced in Irish and North Seas. In Icelandic waters strict harvesting controls (25% of spawning stock) and measures to protect juveniles are in force and management is considered by ICES to be consistent with Precautionary Approach. Moratorium on fishing for cod in waters managed by NAFO since collapse of the fishery in 1992.
Fishery and marine ecosystem related issues	By-catch - cod forms part of a complex mixed demersal fishery which includes whiting, coley (saithe) and haddock. Cod also taken as by-catch in other fisheries for sole, plaice and Nephrops for example; overfishing – stock collapse; discarding; cod vulnerable to effects of global-warming such as increases in sea temperature.
Health, welfare and socio-economic related issues	Cod liver-oil, rich in vitamin A & D, is used for the manufacture of capsules to alleviate conditions such as arthritis and promote general health and well-being; voluntary consumer boycott of Icelandic fishery products likely if country decides to cull whales to protect fish stocks.
Product details	Cod is a versatile fish and is sold fresh (whole or gutted), dried, frozen or salted. Very popular cooked in batter with chips! Frozen and chilled products include fish fingers, fish cakes, fillets, steaks and loins, in breadcrumbs, batter or sauce e.g. parsley and cheese. Cod roe eaten both fresh and smoked. In Japan, Korea, Norway and Iceland cod milt or sperm is eaten.
Season	June to February

Coley

Common and scientific names	Coley; Saithe; black pollack; coalfish; billet; black jack *(Pollachius virens)*
Species detail	Coley, or saithe, belongs to the same family as cod and haddock (Gadidae). It is an active gregarious fish occurring in inshore and offshore waters. Lives close to the seabed. Usually enters coastal waters in spring and returns to deeper water in winter. Immature saithe remain inshore until 3-4 years old. As with most fish migrations for spawning are known to occur. Spawns from January to April in depths of 100-200m. Eggs carried to shallower nursery areas. Dark green in colour, can grow up to 130 cm. Mostly captured at 60-80cm. Can reach ages of more than 25 years.
Species distribution	Widely distributed in the North Atlantic. Important commercial stocks in the North Atlantic including North Sea, West of Scotland, Baltic, Arctic, Greenland, Iceland and Faroes.
Species and/ or stock status	North Sea saithe is outside safe biological limits and catches are dominated by immature fish. Many stocks at low levels of spawning stock biomass (SSB).
Method of capture	Trawls and seines. Also gillnets, hook and line and long-line. Also taken by anglers.
Management	Species managed by restriction through system of TACs and quotas and technical measures in EU waters. MLS 35 cms (30cms in Skaggerrak/Kategat). Harvesting controls in operation in Icelandic & Norwegian waters.
Fishery and marine ecosystem related issues	By-catch – coley forms part of a complex mixed demersal fishery as for cod; discards; stock depletion. Coley also taken in industrial fisheries – although most is recovered for human consumption.
Health, welfare and socio-economic related issues	No specific issues
Product details	Marketed fresh or frozen in fillets or portions in breadcrumbs, sauce etc.
Season	May to February

Cuttlefish

Common and scientific names	Cuttlefish or common cuttlefish *(Sepia officinalis)*
Species detail	Cuttlefish belong to a specialised group of molluscs known as cephalopods which includes octopus and squid. It has a cylinder-shaped body bearing lateral fins. The mouth is surrounded by 8 arms and 2 tentacles. Length up to 30 cm. It has an internal shell or cuttlebone used for buoyancy (these are often found washed up on beaches). Colours are variable – a cuttlefish can instantly match the colour of the seabed it swims over. From birth, young cuttlefish can display at least 13 types of body pattern. In common with other cephalopods it has an ink sack and will squirt ink into the water as a protection measure when threatened. Unlike other molluscs which have nerve centres scattered around the body, in cuttlefish they are fused and enlarged to form a sophisticated brain. Cuttlefish are capable of sophisticated behaviour and have the ability to learn and remember for weeks. It lives over sand and in bays and esturaries. Cuttlefish move into shallow coastal waters to breed in spring and summer. Females only breed once and die soon after laying their eggs known as 'sea grapes'.
Species distribution	Distributed throughout Mediterranean, Atlantic, English Channel and North Seas.
Species and/ or stock status	No specific information available.
Method of capture	Taken as target species in cuttlefish traps and as by-catch in trawl fisheries. Caught in pots throughout Iberia and Meditteranean.
Management	No specific management regime – unprotected species.
Fishery and marine ecosystem related issues	Over-fishing of juveniles before they have had a chance to breed; eggs, often laid on ropes attached to shellfish creels or pots, may be removed from the sea before hatching when the pots are hauled, causing potential problems for reproduction.
Health, welfare and socio-economic related issues	No specific issues
Product details	Cuttlefish are eaten fresh, whole and boiled or cooked. Popular in Mediterranean. Cuttlebone used in petshop trade for budgerigars to sharpen their beaks. Cuttlefish ink also used as a food dye e.g. pasta. Sepia or cuttlefish ink was once used as an artists ink.
Season	May - October

Dab

Common and scientific names	Dab *(Limanda limanda)*. Flounder also used which is confusing as this is a different species (see p. 56).
Species detail	Dab belongs to a large family *(Pleuronectidae)* of right-eyed flatfishes which all have both eyes on the right side of the body. It can reach a length of 40 cm and an age of 10-12 years old. It spawns in spring and early summer and becomes sexually mature at 2-3 years. Young fish live in shallow water and adults move inshore in the summer in a seasonal migration. Feeds mainly on crustaceans and small fish.
Species distribution	Distributed throughout north-east Atlantic – Bay of Biscay to Iceland and Norway; Barents, White and Baltic Seas. Dab is an extremely abundant fish on shallow, sandy grounds off coasts of northern Europe.
Species and/ or stock status	No specific information available.
Method of capture	Caught mainly in trawls and Danish seines.
Management	Managed by system of TACs and quotas (TAC includes flounder) in Norwegian and North seas. No MLS.
Fishery and marine ecosystem related issues	Because the species has little commercial value many are likely to be discarded.
Health, welfare and socio-economic related issues	No specific issues
Product details	Sold fresh, whole or gutted. Dab, when fresh, is considered by some to have the best flavour of all the flatfishes.
Season	September - May

Dogfish

Common and scientific names	Dogfish (or piked or spiny dogfish); Huss; or Spurdog (*Squalus acanthius*).
Species detail	Dogfish are elasmobranchs and belong to the same family as sharks and rays. Possibly the most abundant living shark the dogfish is a spiny or squalid shark. It has a rough skin and a spine at the front of both dorsal fins. Spines can inflict toxic wounds. The dogfish gives birth to live young. Gestation lasts between 18 and 22 months. It matures at 55-61 cm for males and 75-80 cms for females. Found in coastal and offshore waters of northern Europe. Other species sold as dogfish are nursehound (*Scyliorhinus stellaris*) and lesser-spotted catshark (*Scyliorhinus canicula*). Nursehounds and catshark are similar to each other but are differentiated by the shape of their nostril flaps. Both species lay eggs enclosed in smooth rounded cases (known as mermaids purses). Both species belong to the family of dogfishes or *Scyliorhinidae* and have smooth skin. Dogfish is much more important commercially than either nursehound or catshark.
Species distribution	Distributed throughout eastern and western Atlantic, including the Mediterranean and Black seas. Western and Eastern Pacific. Not found in tropical waters. Swims in unisex schools.
Species and/ or stock status	Fished populations in the North Atlantic have a history of over-exploitation followed by near-collapse. Species assessed as at Lower Risk (close to meeting threatened thresholds) by IUCN.
Method of capture	By-catch in trawl, net and line fisheries. Also taken in directed line and trawl fisheries.
Management	TAC proposed for this species in the North Sea. Fishery currently unregulated and species unprotected despite over-exploitation.
Fishery and marine ecosystem related issues	Dogfish, an important and wide-ranging commercial species, is particularly vulnerable to overfishing because of its late maturity, low reproductive capacity and longevity. Likely that pregnant females are taken in fishery and unborn young or pups discarded when animal is gutted.
Health, welfare and socio-economic related issues	No specific issues
Product details	Sold as rock salmon, flake or huss steaks or fillets. These may be marinated, grilled, fried or baked. Flake is the popular name for it sold battered and deep-fried in fish and chip shops. Also utilised for its liver oil and skin which is historically used for leather and as sandpaper.
Season	All year.

Dover Sole

Common and scientific names	Dover, common, black or true sole *(Solea solea)*
Species detail	Sole belongs to the family of flat fishes known as *Soleidae*. Like other right-eyed flat fish they pass through a metamorphosis in their development when one eye (the left) migrates over the top of the head and comes to lie beside the other on the right hand side. It is a nocturnal feeder and spawns in spring and early summer in shallow coastal water. Adults migrate into shallow water during summer months and into deeper water in winter. Up to 30 – 40 cm when adult. Max length 60- 70 cm weight 3 kgs. Maximum reported age 40 years. It is normally a nocturnal feeder on mainly small crustaceans and worms.
Species distribution	Distributed throughout eastern Atlantic; Mediterranean, English Channel, North Sea and west Baltic. Also south to Senegal including Cape Verde Islands. Sole is at its northern most limit around the British Isles. Important stocks in Bay of Biscay, North Sea, Bristol & English Channel, Irish Sea, and Azores. Wadden Sea is the most important spawning area.
Species and/ or stock status	The most abundant member of the sole family the common sole is an important and valuable food-fish. TACs were reduced in many areas between 2000 and 2001, but increased in English Channel and Irish Sea.
Method of capture	Mainly in trawls. Also beam trawls and in set nets. Farming of Dover sole proved difficult as they seemed to like only fresh, live food, not processed, and there was a poor survival rate.
Management	Species managed by restriction through system of TACs and quotas and technical measures in EU waters. MLS 24cm.
Fishery and marine ecosystem related issues	No specific issues
Health, welfare and socio-economic related issues	No specific issues
Product details	Sole is eaten fresh, whole and cooked, usually grilled. Species favoured by the French because of its superb flavour. Slip sole or tongue is used to describe a small Dover sole less than 340 g.
Season	No information available.

Flounder

Common and scientific names	Flounder; Fluke (*Platichthys flesus*)
Species detail	Similar in general appearance to the plaice, flounder is a right-eyed flat fish (70% of eyes found on right). It lives on sandy and muddy bottoms feeding on a range of invetebrate species. Juveniles live in shallow coastal waters & estuaries which are also the summer feeding grounds of the adults. During winter, adults move into deeper, warmer waters where they spawn in the spring. Attains a length of 50-60cm and can live for 15 years.
Species distribution	A widespread European fish found throughout the eastern Atlantic. Also found in freshwater rivers and lakes adjoining with the sea.
Species and/ or stock status	Flounder is not an important food-fish. No information available on stock status as the species is not assessed in Europe.
Method of capture	Of commercial interest in Northern Europe especially in the Baltic Sea. Taken by anglers and as by-catch in trawl nets.
Management	An EU quota exists for dab and lemon sole in Norwegian and North seas which includes flounder – but no distinction appears to be made between species. No MLS specified.
Fishery and marine ecosystem related issues	No specific issues. Introduced to the USA and Canada accidentally through transport in ballast water.
Health, welfare and socio-economic related issues	Flounders living in polluted estuaries e.g. Mersey are vulnerable to heavy metal contamination.
Product details	Sold fresh whole or gutted. Eaten whole on the bone or filleted.
Season	March - November

Grey Mullet

Common and scientific names	Grey mullet or thicklip grey mullet *(Chelon labrosus)*.
Species detail	The mullet belongs to a large family of mainly marine fish known as *Mugilidae*. They are found in all tropical and temperate seas and in many tropical areas in freshwater. Three species occur in northern European waters – thick-lipped, Golden and thin-lipped grey mullet. The thick-lipped is the most common inhabitant of marine coastal waters in Europe. It is found close inshore in harbours and estuaries. It migrates to spawn. Tagging evidence suggests that the same fish inhabit the same area from year to year. Only about 50% of stock is reported to spawn each year – females are unlikely to spawn until their 10th year, then perhaps only one year in three. *Mugilidaes* feed on algae and organic rich materials. Attains a length of 70-75 cm. Reported age 25 years. Reproduction occurs in the sea during winter.
Species distribution	Thick-lipped grey mullet is distributed throughout the eastern Atlantic: Scandinavia and Iceland south to Senegal and Cape Verde Islands. Also Mediterranean and parts of the Black sea. It is a common inhabitant of coastal waters in Europe except most northern parts.
Species and/ or stock status	No specific information available due to lack of scientific data.
Method of capture	Hook and line also gill net and seine-net. A popular sport fish with anglers because of their strength and stamina.
Management	No specific management regime. Local Sea Fishery Committees may specify MLS.
Fishery and marine ecosystem related issues	Grey mullet is slow-growing and therefore vulnerable to over-exploitation. Substantial numbers of winter spawning stock are taken as by-catch in pair-trawl fishery for European sea bass in western English Channel. In growing recognition of the vulnerability of this long-lived species many angling clubs promote a 'catch and release' policy i.e. fish is returned unharmed to the sea.
Health, welfare and socio-economic related issues	Because of its feeding habits - mullet feeds off organic muds in estuaries and bays, often polluted with PCBs, pesticides and heavy metals, and from sewage outfalls - it is not widely recommended for eating!!
Product details	Bought fresh, whole & gutted. Maybe eaten baked, grilled, poached or marinated. Mullet roe is used in the Mediterranean in the making of taramasalata.
Season	April – November (inshore)

Grouper

Common and scientific names	Grouper. Also known as coral trout. (Various – *Epinephelus, Mycteroperca, Anthias* etc. *spp.*)
Species detail	Groupers belong to the large *Serranidae* family. They are an 'exotic' species imported into the UK from a variety of countries including the Canary Islands, Seychelles, the Middle and Far East and the USA.
Species distribution	A variety of species are found world-wide in temperate and tropical waters such as the Indian Ocean and Eastern Atlantic. Specifically many species are found in shallow water over coral reefs.
Species and/ or stock status	Many of these species are overfished and assessed as Critically Endangered, Endangered or Vulnerable by IUCN. Approximately 23 species of grouper are listed species.
Method of capture	Mainly hook and line or net. Also widespread use of dynamite and cyanide.
Management	Trade in some species may be regulated or restricted by CITES.
Fishery and marine ecosystem related issues	Overfishing; changes to complex reef ecology due to their removal; degradation of coral reefs due to physical damage inflicted by collectors and their gear.; loss of biodiversity. Cyanide is widely used by fishermen in many areas of south east Asia, the Pacific and the Indian Ocean to stun fish such as grouper and wrasse which are then exported for the live reef fish food market. The use of this and other poisons degrades coral reefs.
Health, welfare and socio-economic related issues	Groupers are mainly taken from coastal waters in developing countries where fisheries are subsistence-type fisheries. Fishermen receive very little income for this 'luxury' commodity and local people may be deprived of protein; overfishing of traditional food species; impact of long-distant transport by air.
Product details	Marketed fresh.
Season	All year

Gurnard

Common and scientific names	Red Gurnard (*Aspitrigla cuculus*)
Species detail	Gurnards belong to the *Triglidae* (sea robins) family. Red gurnards are found in shallow waters in depths of 20-250m on a variety of different sea-beds. Classified as a generalist they are characterised by fast growth rate and early sexual maturity at a relativley large size. Occasionally they form schools. It spawns in summer. It is one of the smallest European gurnards attaining a length of 40 cm and a weight of about 900 g. Gurnards use the rays on their pectoral fins to locate food buried in the seabed. They also make audible noises using special muscles attached to the swim-bladder. It is believed that this helps in keeping schools in contact especially at spawning time.
Species distribution	*Triglidae* are distributed world-wide in tropical and temperate seas. There are 6 species known in northern European waters. Red gurnard is most commonly exploited as a food fish. It is widely distributed throughout the Atlantic although not abundant, except locally.
Species and/ or stock status	No information available.
Method of capture	A non-targeted species taken as by-catch in trawl fisheries in inshore waters. Also caught by anglers. (A considerable quantity of grey gurnard (*Eutrigla gurnardus*) is taken in trawl fisheries in deeper offshore waters).
Management	Non-quota species. No specific management regime.
Fishery and marine ecosystem related issues.	No specific issues
Health, welfare and socio-economic related issues	No specific issues
Product details	Marketed fresh (whole).
Season	July to February

Haddock

Common and scientific names	Haddock *(Melanogrammus aeglefinus)*
Species detail	Haddock is a cold-temperate (boreal) species. Growth rates vary with sea temperature. It is a migratory fish, found in inshore shallow waters in summer and in deep water in winter. Undertakes extensive migrations in the Barents Sea and Iceland. Smaller than cod it can attain a maximum length of 76-100 cm. It lives close to the seabed in depths of 40-300m. Haddock spawn between February and June, but mostly in March and April. Can live for more than 20 years.
Species distribution	Important commercial species throughout the North Atlantic. Distribution similar to that of cod. Important commercial stocks in north east Atlantic (same as for cod); Norwegian Sea, North Sea, Faroes, Irish Sea, Biscay etc.
Species and/ or stock status	Many stocks are exploited at very high levels with some outside safe biological limits. Despite fishing level on North Sea stock being too high, the TAC was increased by 54% for 2002! Species assessed as Vulnerable by IUCN.
Method of capture	Trawl net, seine netting, hook and line and long-lines. Experimental farming of this species in Norway and Scotland.
Management	Species managed by system of TACs and quotas and technical measures in EU waters. MLS 30cm (Skagerrak/Kattegat 27cm).
Fishery and marine ecosystem related issues	Overfishing and stock collapse; by-catch – haddock forms part of a complex, mixed demersal fishery including cod, whiting, pollack and saithe.
Health, welfare and socio-economic related issues	No specific issues
Product details	Haddock is marketed fresh (whole or gutted), smoked (Arbroath smokies) or frozen. Frozen or chilled products include fish cakes, fillets, portions in batter or breadcrumbs, cutlets, loins, in sauce or batter etc. Used in kedgeree.
Season	May – February

Hake

Common and scientific names	Hake or European hake (*Merluccius merluccius*)
Species detail	Distinct from gadoids belonging to family *Merluccidae*. Only one species found in European seas. It has a slender body, large head and a well developed jaw and teeth. It is a moderately deep-water fish which lives close to the bottom during the day but moves into mid-water to feed at night. Spawns in spring. Max length 100-180 cm. Weight 11-15 kg. Females mature at 5-6 years at about 50 cm.
Species distribution	Hake is widely distributed along the edge of the continental shelf of most temperate seas. Stocks of commercial interest off Atlantic coast of Europe and western North Africa. Also in the Mediterranean Sea (inc. Aegean) and southern coast of the Black Sea.
Species and/ or stock status	Hake is an important food fish. It has been heavily overfished and is now relatively scarce. Many stocks are at serious risk of collapse. In particular the Northern Hake Stock in EU waters which extends from Skagerrak to the Bay of Biscay.
Method of capture	Bottom otter trawl; mid-water trawl, gill nets long-lines.
Management	Species managed by system of TACs and quotas and technical measures in EU waters. MLS 27 cm (30cm in Skaggerak & Kattegat). Recovery plans developed for hake (2001) in waters managed by EU. Plans include a 74% reduction in quota for the Northern stock.
Fishery and marine ecosystem related issues	Overfishing and stock collapse. In common with other deep-water species hake is vulnerable to over-fishing because it matures late and grows slowly; by-catch of marine mammals.
Health, welfare and socio-economic related issues	World-wide trade in other species (e.g. South-African hake) cause prices of European hake to become depressed when they enter the European market.
Product details	Hake is sold whole, filleted or in steaks, fresh or frozen. It is popular in the Mediterranean, dried and salted as well as fresh.
Season	June - March

Halibut

Common and scientific names	Halibut: Atlantic halibut *(Hippoglossus hippoglossus)*; Greenland or black or mock halibut *(Reinhardtius hippoglossoides)*
Species detail	Both species live in deep cold boreal waters. They are slender-bodied and thickset, right-eyed flatfish. Atlantic halibut is larger than Greenland halibut and can attain a maximum size of 2.5 m – females are larger than males. Spawning takes place in deep water during winter and early spring. After spawning, females move into shallower water. The young fish live close inshore for between 2 & 4 years then gradually move into deeper water until they are sexually mature at 10-14 years. Atlantic halibut can live up to 50 years. Greenland halibut can attain a size of 80 –120 cm and ages of 15-20 years. It spawns in summer. It reaches maturity at 4 years at about 40 cm for males and 8 years at around 60 cm for females.
Species distribution	Atlantic halibut distributed in eastern Atlantic (Bay of Biscay to Spitsbergen, Barents Sea, Iceland and eastern Greenland) and western Atlantic (south-western Greenland and Labrador in Canada to Virginia in USA); Greenland halibut found in deep-water on the continental margin in Arctic, North Pacific and North Atlantic.
Species and/ or stock status	Both species are exploited commercially. Vulnerable to overfishing because of their slow growth rate and late age of sexual maturity. Atlantic species more popular as a food species than the smaller Greenland halibut. Stocks greatly diminished in North Atlantic. Atlantic halibut assessed as Endangered by IUCN.
Method of capture	Long-line; trawl; hook and line. Gill-nets used to target Greenland halibut.
Management	EU TAC for Greenland halibut *(Reinhardtius hippoglossoides)* only. North West Atlantic Fisheries Organisation (NAFO) responsible for management of Greenland and Atlantic species. Pacific halibut *(Hippoglossus stenolepis)* managed by the International Pacific Halibut Commission (IPHC)
Fishery and marine ecosystem related issues	Atlantic halibut in particular is a slow growing and long-lived species and vulnerable to overfishing and stock collapse; by-catch of marine wildife in long-line and gill-net fisheries; young halibut may be taken as by-catch in inshore fisheries for other flat fish species.
Health, welfare and socio-economic related issues	Halibut liver-oil, rich in vitamin A & D, is used for the manufacture of capsules to alleviate conditions such as arthritis and promote general health and well-being.
Product details	Sold fresh, gutted and filleted or steaks. Also popular smoked and sliced.
Season	June – March

Herring

Common and scientific names	Herring *(Clupea harengus)*
Species detail	Herring belongs to the same family of clupeids as sprat and pilchard. Apart from sandeels, herring are the only commercially important bony fish species to lay demersal eggs (most lay pelagic eggs which are carried by currents and tides) in British waters. It can grow to 43 cm although size can vary amongst races (distinct breeding stocks). Most landed and sold now are around 25 cm. Individual races make complex feeding and spawning migrations. Some spawn in spring close inshore whilst others spawn in summer and autumn in offshore waters. Young fish form large schools and are common inshore in their first year. Herring is sexually mature at 3-9 years. At least one population in UK waters spawns in any one month of the year.
Species distribution	Widespread species – included in the Guinness Book of Records as the most numerous fish – although now overfished locally. Members of the herring family form one of the most important commercial fisheries resources in the world. Important stocks or races in the east Atlantic are the winter-spawning Norwegian and Icelandic herrings, the autumn spawning Icelandic and North Sea herrings and the Baltic herrings.
Species and/ or stock status	North Sea herring stocks collapsed in the 1970s, resulting in a total fishing ban between 1977 and 1981, and in the 1990s when levels of spawning stock fell to less than 0.5 million tonnes. Emergency measures were introduced and have remained in place to rebuild stocks to levels above minimum acceptable levels.
Method of capture	Purse-seine; mid-water trawls/pair trawls; and drift-nets.
Management	Herring managed by TAC and quotas in EU waters; MLS in EU waters – 20cm (18cm in Skagerrak/Kattegat); managed by RFO International Baltic Sea Fishery Commission (IBSFC) in Baltic seas and by NAFO in NW Atlantic; fishery in Thames Blackwater accredited by the Marine Stewardship Council as an environmentally responsible fishery.
Fishery and marine ecosystem related issues	By-catch of marine mammals; removal of immature fish - young herring are taken in some inshore areas with young sprat and sold as 'whitebait'; by-catch of herring in capelin and other industrial fisheries; industrial fisheries for herring; herring are major converters of plankton and therefore an important prey species in marine ecosystems.
Health, welfare and socio-economic related issues	Herring is an oily fish rich in omega 3.
Product details	Herring are sold fresh – whole or filleted, gutted or ungutted. Also smoked (kipper), marinated, canned or bottled in brine or oil. Preserved herring in its many forms is popular in Scandanavia and in Holland in particular e.g. Rollmop (onion and herring in strong vinegar solution). Because herring is oily, fresh fish is best grilled, fried or baked. Also taken in industrial fisheries for fish-meal and oil. Marine Stewardship Council labelled products available.
Season	May – December

Hoki

Common and scientific names	Hoki or Blue grenadier *(Macruronus novaezelandiae)*. Hoki is a Maori name meaning 'to return'
Species detail	Hoki belongs to the hake family *Merlucciidae*. It is a deep-water fish found only in the southern hemisphere. Adults occur in waters deeper than 400 m while juveniles are found in shallower water. It can grow up to 120 cm (typical length is 60-100 cm) and is reported to live to 25 years. Hoki matures at 4-7 years.
Species distribution	Hoki is distributed throughout the south-west Pacific in waters off New Zealand and southern Australia and is one of the most abundant fish found in New Zealand waters.
Species and/ or stock status	Stocks in New Zealand waters are reported to be well managed and are currently above safe biological limits.
Method of capture	Hoki is caught by trawling at depths of 200 – 800 m.
Management	Stocks managed by the Government with jurisdiction over the waters of the relevant Exclusive Economic or Fishing Zone e.g. New Zealand and Australian. New Zealand hoki is certified as an environmentally responsible fishery by the Marine Stewardship Council. Hoki is also exploited outside NZ jurisdiction and so not all hoki fisheries are certified.
Fishery and marine ecosystem related issues	In common with all deep-water fish, hoki are prone to over-exploitation if the fishery is not managed responsibly. Deep-water species mature late and grow very slowly.
Health, welfare and socio-economic related issues	No specific issues
Product details	Available in block, natural and formed portions, skin-on fillets and skinned and boned fillets. Marine Stewardship Council labelled products available including breaded fillets.
Season	Not known

John Dory

Common and scientific names	John Dory (*Zeus faber*)
Species detail	John Dory is a member of the *Zeidae* family. It usually lives a solitary life or is found in small schools in inshore waters (10-50 m). Dory also reported to live in a range of depths from 200 m to close to the surface. The species has a highly compressed body, with large dark spots surrounded by a light ring on each side and long anterior rays extending from the dorsal fin. Dory has a protrusible mouth with which to engulf its prey. It reproduces at the end of winter/start of spring in the north-east Atlantic. In the English Channel it spawns in summer. It reaches maximum lengths of 40-60 cm and ages of 12 years.
Species distribution	Zeidae or Dories have a world-wide distribution in temperate and warm-temperate seas, mostly in shallow water but some are also found in the deep sea. John Dory is distributed throughout the eastern Atlantic, Norway to South Africa, also Mediterranean and Black Sea.
Species and/ or stock status	No information available. No specific fishery for this species.
Method of capture	Generally taken as by-catch in trawls. It is a valuable species but its habits are such that landings are rare.
Management	No specific management regime. Non-quota and non-protected species.
Fishery and marine ecosystem related issues	No specific issues, however landing and marketing of immature fish is possible.
Health, welfare and socio-economic related issues	No specific issues
Product details	Sold fresh and frozen. May be steamed, fried, boiled or baked. Also used in Mediterranean stew (bouillabaise).
Season	All year

Langoustine

Common and scientific names	Langoustine; Scampi; Dublin Bay prawn; Norway lobster (Nephrops norvegicus)
Species detail	Scampi is a crustacean belonging to the Order Decapoda (ten legs). It is much smaller than the common lobster reaching a length of up to 15 cm. It lives in burrows in soft mud or sand from about 50 m downwards. Its diet is varied and includes worms, molluscs, crustaceans and scavenged material. Males grow relatively quickly to around 6 cm, and seldom exceed 10 years old, while females grow more slowly and can reach over 20 years old. Females mature at about 3 years old. In the Autumn the female lays eggs (1-5,000), attached to the tail and carried for about 9 months. Hatching is in the spring. The planktonic larvae are present in the upper water column for 6-8 weeks before settling on the bottom. Species live in discrete populations. Movement may occur between populations during the larval stage but little is known to occur once settlement has taken place.
Species distribution	Distributed throughout the Mediterranean, eastern North Atlantic and North Sea. Also Adriatic. Widespread around Scottish coast and in Irish, Celtic and North Seas.
Species and/ or stock status	Important commercial stocks in North Sea and in waters west of Britain. Langoustine is the most commercially important shellfish species in the UK. Stocks are mostly inside safe biological limits but some are overfished.
Method of capture	Trawl nets (widespread use of 70 mm nets with square mesh panels fitted to allow escape of juveniles and white fish); pots or creel
Management	Managed by TAC and MLS in EU waters. UK takes over 50% of EU quota.
Fishery and marine ecosystem related issues	By-catch and discarding of immature white fish and langoustine in trawl fisheries; overfishing of discrete populations - of males in particular (egg bearing females spend more time in their burrows which provides natural protection to spawning stock).
Health, welfare and socio-economic related issues	Like the lobster they are boiled alive. Tails often removed at sea when animal is alive.
Product details	Eaten fresh whole and cooked, or tails removed and eaten separately. Popular deep-fried in the form of scampi. Widely used in classic French cuisine.
Season	April - November

Lemon Sole

Common and scientific names	Lemon sole *(Microstomus kitt)*
Species detail	Lemon sole is a flatfish species living on mostly stony bottoms. It is a specialist feeder on a variety of small invertebrates – its small mouth limiting the size of its prey. Apparently it does not feed during the winter months. Sexually mature at 3-4 years (males); 4-6 years (females). May live for 17 years. Attains a length of about 66 cm. Spawns in spring and summer.
Species distribution	Distributed throughout north-east Atlantic it is a widespread flatfish in Northern Europe where it is common locally.
Species and/ or stock status	No information available. Although no evidence of overfishing.
Method of capture	Caught mainly in trawls including beam-trawling for flat fish.
Management	Managed by TAC in Norwegian and North Seas only. TAC includes dab and flounder. No distinction made between species.
Fishery and marine ecosystem related issues	Damage to seabed especially by beam trawls.
Health, welfare and socio-economic related issues	No specific issues
Product details	Lemon sole is usually sold whole on the bone or skinned and filleted. It may be cooked on the bone (improves flavour) or filleted and baked or grilled for example. Also sold filleted and frozen in breadcrumbs.
Season	May – March

Ling

Common and scientific names	Ling (*Molva molva*)
Species detail	Ling, the biggest of the gadoid family, are long-bodied cod-like fish. It is essentially a deep- water fish occurring most abundantly in 300-400 m depth, although large numbers live in shallower water. It breeds between March and July. A single female may produce up to 60 million eggs. Can attain a length of 2 m and a weight of 35 kg. Usually 1-1.5 m in inshore waters. Ling reaches sexual maturity at 5-7 years when it is 66-75 cm.
Species distribution	Distributed throughout Atlantic. Principal spawning areas are Bay of Biscay, slopes west of the British Isles and off the Faroes and southern Iceland. Separate stocks in Iceland, Norwegian waters and Faroes.
Species and/ or stock status	In areas where ling is most heavily exploited stocks are considered to be outside safe biological limits.
Method of capture	Mainly caught on long-lines by both commercial fishermen and anglers; also taken as by-catch in trawls and gill-nets.
Management	Managed by TAC and MLS (63 cm) in EU waters. Although NEAFC is responsible for the management of fish stocks in international waters in the north-east Atlantic, ling and other deep-water species are an unregulated resource under the NEAFC Convention.
Fishery and marine ecosystem related issues	Stock collapse – fishing for this species is unrestricted in international waters; by-catch; damage to deep-water ecosystems.
Health, welfare and socio-economic related issues	No specific issues
Product details	Eaten fresh and cooked. Also popular dried and salted. A popular food fish in France.
Season	September - July

Lobster

Common and scientific names	Lobster *(Homarus gammarus)*
Species detail	The lobster's appearance is unmistakable: dark blue shell (turns red when boiled) with pale yellow markings and long red antennae. It has large powerful claws which are different in shape – one (usually the right claw) is heavier and used for crushing, while the other is used as a sharp cutting tool. Lobsters are territorial animals usually living in a crevice or underneath a rock, where they spend most of their time, coming out to feed mainly at night. Mating is thought to occur in late summer, but females can store the sperm packet over the winter so the eggs are not fertilised and laid until the following summer. They may live up to 50 years or more. Body up to 75 cm but rarely more than 30 cm and weight 9 kgs.
Species distribution	The common lobster is found throughout the Mediterranean, Atlantic, English Channel, North Sea and west Baltic.
Species and/ or stock status	Species is overfished in many traditional lobster areas and stocks are now depleted. Fishermen are now extending their grounds into previously un-fished waters but it is only a matter of time before these areas are also seriously depleted. Fishery models suggest that UK stocks are well below a quarter of their potential level in the un-fished state.
Method of capture	Pot or creel.
Management	Managed in coastal waters of England and Wales by Sea Fisheries Committee byelaws e.g. V-notching of 'berried' females (see chapter 5). Cornwall SFC involved in the setting up of the first commercial hatchery in England in Padstow, Cornwall. Also hatcheries in Orkney and Anglesey; MLS for lobster in EU (including UK waters) of 87 mm carapace length i.e. the length between the back of the eye socket and the furthest edge of the carapace (shell); proposal to introduce a restrictive licensing scheme for shellfish is under consideration for UK waters, also proposal to prohibit landed of berried lobster and outlaw 'scrubbing' (see below).
Fishery and marine ecosystem related issues	Overfishing and stock depletion – removal rates for lobster from UK coasts are estimated to vary from 20 – 70%; removal of larger breeding animals – large lobster (120-150 mm carapace length) are now rarely found in traditional lobster areas.
Health, welfare and socio-economic related issues	Lobster is often boiled alive. The RSPCA recommend that lobster is placed in a large freezer (-18° C for 2 hours) before being boiled. This will cause the animal to fall asleep and then die. Animals are invariably transported live for freshness; 'Scrubbing' or berried females - the removal of eggs from berried females.
Product details	Sold (sometimes live) and eaten cooked in its shell. Coral or roe of female lobster considered a delicacy.
Season	April - November

Mackerel

Common and scientific names	Mackerel; Atlantic mackerel *(Scomber scombrus)*
Species detail	Mackerel is a fast swimming species of the *scombrid* family, related to the tuna. It lives in mid-water occasionally in huge schools above the continental shelf. Highly migratory moving both inshore and north in summer – the reverse movement occurs in winter. They spawn mainly in March to July. Young fish eat plankton. Adults eat pelagic crustaceans and prey heavily on schools of smaller fish. Mackerel tend to fast during winter months. Can attain a maximum length of 66 cm and weight of 3 kg. More usually 40 cm and 680 g. Can attain an age of more than 20 years old.
Species distribution	Scombrids are found world-wide in tropical and warm temperate seas and mackerel is a common fish in the North Atlantic.
Species and/ or stock status	Mackerel is an important food fish. Important commercial stocks in north, east and western Atlantic. North-east Atlantic stock includes North Sea, Western and Southern stocks. Whilst Western and Southern stocks are considered inside safe biological limits the Western stock is considered to be harvested at too high a rate. The North Sea stock has long been depleted. Main mackerel catching nations are Norway, UK, Ireland, Netherlands and Russia.
Method of capture	Purse-seine; pelagic trawl; handline fisheries common in SW England (Cornwall and Devon) - one purse-seiner may take as much as 1,800 tonnes of fish per week as much as the entire SW hand-line fleet removes in one year! Handline fishery in SW England certified by Marine Stewardship Council (MSC) as an environmentally responsible fishery.
Management	Managed by TAC - UK has just under 50% share of the EU quota for this species - and MLS in EU waters – 20 cm in all areas except North Sea which is 30 cm; EC seasonal closure in North Sea; 'Mackerel Box' (area in which directed fishing is restricted) off SW England created in 1981 for protection of juvenile mackerel.
Fishery and marine ecosystem related issues	Pelagic trawl fisheries associated with by-catch of marine mammals (dolphin prey on mackerel) in UK waters; by-catch and discarding or 'slipping' of juveniles. Also concern for by-catch of juvenile mackerel in fisheries for pilchard and horse mackerel in 'Mackerel Box' in Western waters.
Health, welfare and socio-economic related issues	Mackerel is an oily fish rich in Omega-3; SW hand-line fleet (approx. 100 boats) is labour intensive employing over 300 in small coastal-communities.
Product details	Mackerel is best eaten fresh. It is sold whole or filleted and is suitable for grilling, braising and baking. Also frozen, canned and smoked. MSC labelled products available at Sainsbury & Tesco.
Season	All year

Marlin

Common and scientific names	Marlin or billfish: Atlantic Blue *(Makaira nigricans)* ; Atlantic White *(Tetrapturus albidus)*
Species detail	Marlin belong to the family *Istiophoridae*. There are 4 species of which 2 are found in the Atlantic - the blue and white marlin. White marlin is the smallest of the species. They feed on squid and fish. Usually solitary animals found in deep blue-water they are highly migratory travelling long distances. White marlin can reach 300 cm and blue marlin 500 cm.
Species distribution	Found in tropical and temperate waters of Atlantic, Pacific and Indian Oceans.
Species and/ or stock status	Both Atlantic species are at low levels. The white marlin is the most threatened and is in danger of extinction. Atlantic stocks of white marlin have declined by 77% between 1966 and 1991 and by 40% between 1980 and 1990. Conservationists and scientists recently filed a petition with the National Federation of Marine Services (NFMS) in the USA to have white marlin listed under the US Endangered Species Act.
Method of capture	Long-line; gill-net and purse-seine. Also taken in recreational fisheries – highly prized sport or game fish.
Management	International Commission for the Conservation of Atlantic Tuna (ICCAT) has responsibility for management of tuna and tuna-like species including marlin in international waters on high seas. ICCAT assessment in 2000 indicates that blue marlin stock level is at 40% of maximum sustainable yield and white marlin at 15%. Neither stock is predicted to recover if current levels of mortality continue.
Fishery and marine ecosystem related issues	Over-fishing and stock collapse – Atlantic white and blue marlin both threatened with collapse; juvenile marlin discarded in more valuable fisheries for swordfish and tuna ; by-catch of sharks, marine turtles and mammals in long-line fisheries; marlin and swordfish etc. are large predatory animals at the top of the marine food chain, their removal therefore has implications for stability of marine ecology.
Health, welfare and socio-economic related issues	No specific issues
Product details	Marlin is eaten fresh in steaks. It may be marinated and baked or grilled. Also available smoked. In Japan it is used in Sashimi (sliced raw fish). Also marketed frozen.
Season	All year

Megrim

Common and scientific names	Megrim, grey sole or whiff (*Lepidorhombus whiffiagonis*)
Species detail	Another left-eyed flat-fish species found on the lower continental shelf. Megrim spawns in spring in deep water off Iceland and west of British Isles, the eggs are transparent and pelagic. It attains a length of about 60cm although usually 35-45cm.
Species distribution	A common flat fish species found in shelf seas throughout the north-east Atlantic.
Species and/ or stock status	Only the west coast (western) stocks are assessed and these are considered to be within safe biological limits but harvested at an unsustainable level. Important commercial species for Spain, France and UK.
Method of capture	Taken mainly as by-catch in trawl fisheries and now an important commercial species in its own right.
Management	Managed by a system of TACs and quotas in EU waters. MLS 20 cm (25cm in Skagerrak & Kattegat).
Fishery and marine ecosystem related issues	No specific issues
Health, welfare and socio-economic related issues	No specific issues
Product details	Sold fresh and whole or filleted. Comparable to plaice in flavour.
Season	May - March

Monkfish

Common and scientific names	Monkfish or angler fish (*Lophius piscatorius*)
Species detail	Anglerfish are so called because they possess a fishing lure at the tip of a specially modified dorsal ray with which they can entice prey. They have a very large mouth and sharp, distinctive, recurved teeth. They live on the seabed on sandy and rocky bottoms from the coast down to 1,000 m. Monkfish can attain a maximum length of 2 m (females) and a weight of around 40 kg. Males do not grow beyond 1m. Spawning takes place in spring and early summer in deep water to the west of Scotland. Eggs are released in a gelatinous raft or 'egg veil' which floats in the surface layers and can reach in excess of 10 m length. Monkfish reach sexual maturity at about 70 cm in females, at about 9-11 years of age and 50 cm for males, at around 6 years of age.
Species distribution	Distributed throughout the north-east Atlantic including the Mediterranean and Black Sea.
Species and/ or stock status	Monkfish is particularly vulnerable to over-exploitation because of its life-history characteristics. There is general consensus amongst scientists that there is only one stock and that this spawns in deep-water to the west of Scotland. Levels of fishing in these waters is too high. Monkfish commands a very high market value and is one of the most lucrative species to catch. Therefore commercial interest and fishing effort on this species is likely to remain high. In Shetland waters it is estimated that on average 55% of males and 92% of females are immature when caught. Mature females are now extremely rare.
Method of capture	Targeted in trawl and gill-net fisheries. Also taken as by-catch in trawl fisheries.
Management	Managed by TAC only in EU waters. No MLS specified. UK and French fishermen have the major share of quota for this species in the north-east Atlantic. Of significant commercial importance to Scottish fishermen.
Fishery and marine ecosystem related issues	Species vulnerable to over-exploitation because of its slow growth and high age at first maturity; overfishing especially of immature females; by-catch of deep-water species in trawl fisheries; damage to deep-water flora and fauna; misreporting i.e. some fishermen record catches as taken from the west of Scotland when in fact they came from the North Sea and vice versa. Misreporting distorts data upon which scientific and management (quotas) advice is made.
Health, welfare and socio-economic related issues	No specific issues
Product details	Only the fleshy tails are eaten, usually skinned and cooked. Head used to make soup (boullabaise) in Mediterranean countries.
Season	All year

Mussels

Common and scientific names	Blue or Common mussel *(Mytilus edulis)*. Also Green-lipped mussel imported from New Zealand.
Species detail	Common mussels are bivalve molluscs found around our shores from mid-shore down to about 20 m or more below low-water mark. They normally live in large aggregations, attaching themselves to the rocks and each other with sticky threads known as byssus. The size and shape vary widely, but the colour is always deep bluish- purple. Shell up to 10 cm long but usually much smaller. Mussels become sexually mature when one year old and may live to 10-15 years or more. In addition to our native mussel, New Zealand green-lipped mussels from the Pacific are imported.
Species distribution	Widespread on stones and rocks in estuaries, on rocks on more exposed shores and often in extensive beds from middle shore downward. Distributed throughout Mediterranean, North Atlantic, English Channel, North Sea and Baltic coasts.
Species and/ or stock status	Mussels are widely cultivated and stocks generally considered to be under-exploited. Production from natural and cultivated beds. Fisheries located in sheltered estuaries and bays such as The Wash, Morecambe Bay and Menai Strait, North Wales.
Method of capture	Dredged also cultivated widely; commonly grown by bottom culture or rope-hanging or floating culture. Rope hanging culture widespread method in Spain, Ireland and Scotland. In New Zealand Green-lipped mussels are widely cultivated by rope-hanging method.
Management	Cultivated beds managed by Several and Regulating Orders (see chapter 5), wild beds may be managed by Sea Fishery Committee byelaws.
Fishery and marine ecosystem related issues	Mussel cultivation is an extensive, low impact method of mariculture. Some environmental impacts mainly associated with removal of seed from natural mussel beds. However, extensive cultivation has increased abundance of mussel and therefore availability of seed.
Health, welfare and socio-economic related issues	Mussels are filter-feeders and can accumulate toxins in their flesh. However, water quality standards for shellfish (bivalve & gastropod molluscs) for human consumption is controlled and may only be harvested commercially from designated shellfish growing areas; Long-distance transport (by air or ship) of New Zealand Green-lipped mussels; Mussels cooked alive in their shells.
Product details	Usually sold live and eaten cooked in their shells. May be smoked. Known as moules in France, served as moules mariniere cooked in wine and garlic. Also used for bait by anglers.
Season	September - March

Octopus

Common and scientific names	Octopus: Common octopus *(Octopus vulgaris)*; Lesser octopus *(Eledone cirrhosa)*
Species detail	Octopus belong to the same family (cephalopods) as cuttlefish and squid. They differ in that they have no skeleton. This allows them to squeeze through nooks and crannies in rocks amongst which they live. Two species are found in British waters – common and lesser octopus. Vulgaris has a double row of suckers while Eledone has a single row. Octopus often live in 'lairs' where stones have been arranged for camouflage and protection. Colour change or camouflage plays an important part in life. Animals tend to resemble the background against which they live. Like all cephalopods, octopods grow rapidly and are probably 3 to 4 years old when sexually mature. Reproduction occurs in summer. In copulation the male extends the modified 4th arm into the mantle cavity of the female where it deposits spermatophore or sperm packets. Females lay up to 150,000 eggs and guard them before dying after they are hatched. The span of the arms in Eldone does not usually exceed 70 cm but may be up to four times this in Vulgaris.
Species distribution	Common octopus is found in more southerly waters throughout the Mediterranean and Atlantic north as far as the English Channel and into the southern North Sea. Also found off African and Central American Coasts and may be found in the English Channel in high numbers after a mild winter. The lesser octopus is found in more northern waters of the Atlantic including the English Channel and northern North Sea. Bressing is dependent upon water temperature. Most northerly breeding stocks are those off Brittany.
Species and/ or stock status	No information available.
Method of capture	Usually rounded earthenware pots which they enter instinctively in order to hide. A number of pots maybe dangled in the water on lines. Also taken as by-catch in trawl nets and by divers in some parts of the world.
Management	No management at all in Northern Europe.
Fishery and marine ecosystem related issues	Over-exploitation of local and juvenile populations.
Health, welfare and socio-economic related issues	Octopus are intelligent animals and have an elaborate central nervous system. They have a memory, and can be taught to differentiate between objects. Octopus have well-developed eyes similar to humans. For this reason they are often used in 'animal' experiments. As vivisection laws only apply to vertebrates, invertebrates such as octopods have no protection.
Product details	Eaten fresh and cooked. Beak, eyes and ink sac are removed before cooking. Ink may be used in cooking as a food dye. Juvenile octopus now more commonly available in UK. Octopus is a delicacy in Iberia, the Mediterranean and Japan.
Season	May – December

Orange Roughy

Common and scientific names	Orange Roughy (Hoplostethus atlanticus)
Species detail	Orange roughy is a berycoid belonging to the family Trachichthyidae (slimeheads). These are deep-water oceanic fish found along the lower continental shelf. Roughy inhabit deep (900 – 1,000 m), cold waters, over steep continental slopes, ocean ridges and sea mounts. It is a deep-bodied, orange coloured fish which has very slow growth, great longevity – it is one of the longest lived fish known and may live for 125 years - and low fecundity. Natural mortality and reproductive output is low as mature fish do not spawn every year. Spawning occurs in North Atlantic from January - Febuary. Orange roughy is a sedentary species with an approx. size of 50-75 cm and max. weight of 7 kg. Length at first maturity is 48 cm in males; 52 cm in females. It feeds on crustaceans, squid and fish.
Species distribution	Distributed throughout West Atlantic: Gulf of Maine; East Atlantic: Iceland to Morocco; Namibia, South Africa; Indonesian Pacific: southern-central Indian Ocean, New Zealand; East Pacific: Chile.
Species and/ or stock status	No fisheries management of Atlantic stocks of orange roughy so stocks are considered by ICES to be over-exploited and 'outside safe biological limits'. Orange roughy is one of the most vulnerable deep-water species, for which the sustainable catch level should only be a small proportion of the virgin (or unfished) biomass. In NZ waters, stocks have been reduced by at least 80% of their original biomass.
Method of capture	Bottom trawling, gillnetting and long-lining. Species are targeted when they come together to spawn.
Management	Currently no adequate monitoring, management or protection of orange roughy and other deep-water fish stocks. NEAFC is responsible for management of fisheries in NE Atlantic, but the Convention does not include regulation of this or other deep-water species.
Fishery and marine ecosystem related issues	Overfishing and stock collapse – species particularly vulnerable to over-exploitation as it is long-lived, slow growing with high age at first maturity and low fecundity. Fished populations take a long time to recover; destruction of deep-water habitat - seamounts and coral banks vulnerable to damage by fishing gears; impact on deep-water ecology about which very little is known.
Health, welfare and socio-economic related issues	No specific issues
Product details	Marketed: fresh or frozen. Eaten: marinated and/or steamed, fried or baked. Wax esters and oils in muscle once used in cosmetics, pharmaceuticals and high grade lubricants.
Season	All year

Oyster

Common and scientific names	Native Oyster or common, European or flat oyster *(Ostrea edulis)*. Pacific oyster *(Crassostrea gigas)* is introduced non-native species.
Species detail	The native or flat oyster is a filter feeding, bivalve mollusc. Found in shallow water down to about 80 m where there is suitable substrate and in commercial beds. The native oyster develops initially as a male then changes its sex bi-annually. In Britain, breeding normally takes place in the summer. Each animal spawns twice, once as a male and once as a female. Shell up to 10 cm. Shape variable.
Species distribution	Native oyster has a wide geographical range from Norway along the coast of Europe as far as Spain to Morocco on the Atlantic coast.
Species and/ or stock status	Throughout much of Britain the native oyster is severely depleted in the wild. Two hundred years of over-exploitation, pests, disease (introduced with non-native species), pollution (mainly Tributyltin (TBT)) and harsh winters have contributed to its demise. Former large native oyster populations on eastern side of Britain and in off-shore waters e.g. Dogger Bank now lost and many others e.g. Swansea Bay depleted. The Solent in Hampshire is now the largest and one of few wild native oyster producing areas in the UK.
Method of capture	Gathered or raked by hand. Also dredged – off-shore beds only. Areas once noted for their large natural beds are now being used for oyster farming or cultivation including non-native species such as Pacific oyster *(Crassotrea gigas)* which are currently more widely cultivated than the native oyster (see Chapter 5).
Management	There is a closed season to protect wild native oysters in the spawning season; fisheries are generally privately owned and managed by Several and Regulating Orders (chapter 5); the native oyster is the subject of a Biodiversity Action Plan (BAP) (Chapter 6) which aims to maintain and expand, where possible, the distribution and abundance of native oyster in UK waters. The Shellfish Association of Great Britain (SAGB) has responsibility for implementing the plan.
Fishery and marine ecosystem related issues	Many native oysters beds now over-exploited – exploitation reached a peak in 1864 when 700 million oysters were consumed in London alone. Now active farming of native oyster is developing, particularly on Scotland's west coast.
Health, welfare and socio-economic related issues	Oysters are filter feeders and can accumulate toxins in their flesh. However, water quality standards for shellfish (bivalve & Gastropod molluscs) for human consumption is controlled and may only be harvested commercially from designated shellfish growing areas. Oysters, rich in zinc, are attributed aphrodisiac properties. Low zinc levels are associated with depression, tiredness and loss of libido.
Product details	Mainly eaten raw and alive from their shells.
Season	Native oyster not available during closed season (during spawning) (14th May - 4th Aug). Pacific oyster – available all year.

Pilchard

Common and scientific names	Pilchard or European pilchard (*Sardina pilchardus*). Small fish are called sardines.
Species detail	Pilchard is a pelagic schooling fish and a member of the herring family (*Clupeidae*). It reaches the northern extreme of its range around SW England. Spawns in spring and summer in open sea. Females produce 50-60,000 eggs. Eggs and larvae are pelagic. After spawning it migrates northwards and is then found inshore in coastal waters. It can attain a length of 25 cm. Maximum reported age is 15 years.
Species distribution	European pilchard is distributed in the north-east Atlantic: from Iceland (rare) and North Sea, southward to Senegal, western Mediterranean, Adriatic, Mamara and Black Seas. Its distribution and abundance is closely related to environmental (temperature) variations. During warm periods it is numerous in the English Channel and southern North Sea. Elsewhere, other pilchard species are found in cool plankton-rich waters. Major stocks are found off Japan, in the eastern Pacific, south-west Africa, Australia and New Zealand. The largest pilchard fisheries are for related genera in the Pacific and off southern Africa.
Species and/ or stock status	No specific information available for European pilchard. Young fish are heavily fished off the Biscay coast and off Portugal; they are canned as sardines. The fishery off the Cornish coast waxes and wanes. Fishing for pilchard and horse mackerel continues in the 'Mackerel Box' - a conservation area to protect juvenile mackerel.
Method of capture	Purse-seine; mid-water and bottom pair trawls.
Management	In EU waters pilchard is a non-pressure stock i.e. there is no quota specified for this species. A MLS of 11 cm is specified for sardines taken in all EU waters.
Fishery and marine ecosystem related ssues	By-catch of (juvenile) mackerel in fisheries for pilchard off SW England; by-catch of marine mammals in purse-seines and mid-water trawls; small, possibly immature fish, eaten as sardines; pilchard species also basis for industrial fisheries in certain parts of the world e.g. Menhaden, USA.
Health, welfare and socio-economic related issues	Oily fish rich in omega 3. Sardines rich in calcium as they are eaten whole including bones.
Product details	Marketed fresh, frozen or canned. Canned as pilchards (usually in tomatoe sauce) or as sardines in brine or olive oil etc. Traditional 'Star Gazey Pie' made with pilchards originates from Cornwall.
Season	November - April

Plaice

Common and scientific names	Plaice (*Pleuronectes platessa*)
Species detail	Plaice belongs to a large family of right-eyed flatfishes called *Pleuronectidae*. Most are shallow-water, bottom-dwelling fishes, some are found in deeper water on the upper continental shelf. Plaice is a bottom dwelling fish found on sandy bottoms in depths up to 50 m. Older fish live in deeper water whilst young fish are commonly found in intertidal pools and inshore nurseries. The Wadden Sea is an important nursery area. Plaice spawn in the early months of the year (January-March) and sometimes make long spawning migrations. Spawning takes place in well defined areas. North Sea plaice reach between 35 and 45 cm in their 6th year. A long-lived species, becoming sexually mature at 3-7 years (female) 2-6 years (male) and living as long as 30 years. Plaice are active at night and remain buried in the sand during the day.
Species distribution	Widely distributed in cool temperate waters of the north-east Atlantic. Important stocks in Skagerrak/Kattegat; Norwegian Sea; Icelandic waters; North Sea; and Irish Sea.
Species and/ or stock status	An important flatfish for fisheries in Europe. Heavy fishing has meant that large plaice are very rare. North Sea and Channel stocks are outside safe biological limits or fishing level is too high. Irish Sea stock still inside safe biological limits.
Method of capture	Caught mainly in trawls, including beam trawls, and Danish seines, but can also be captured in set nets. Commonly caught by anglers.
Management	Managed by TAC and quota in EU waters. MLS 22cm (27cm in Skagerrak and Kattegat)
Fishery and marine ecosystem related issues	Overfishing – especially of immature fish and stock collapse. Plaice susceptible to changes in environmental conditions; beam trawling cause damage to seabed communities.
Health, welfare and socio-economic related issues	No specific issues
Product details	Plaice is sold fresh, whole or filleted and frozen. Popular fried.
Season	May – February

Pollack

Common and scientific names	Pollack or Green Pollack (*Pollachius pollachius*). NB: Alaskan pollock (*Theregra chalcogramma*) is a different species although not included in this Guide it is sold in the UK.
Species detail	A warm temperate species belonging to the cod family. Pollack spawn between January to April in deep water. Young of the first year are particularly common close inshore. Species can reach a maximum length of 120-130cm and an age of more than 8 years. Usually around 50 cm and 4 kg.
Species distribution	Pollack is distributed throughout the north-east Atlantic: Norway, the Faroes and Iceland to the Bay of Biscay. Species widely distributed in European waters, particularly in inshore waters.
Species and/ or stock status	No information available, species not assessed.
Method of capture	Taken as by-catch in directed fisheries for cod and saithe. Also captured on lines and by anglers.
Management	Species managed by restriction through system of TACs and quotas and technical measures in EU waters. MLS 30cm.
Fishery and marine ecosystem related issues	No specific issues
Health, welfare and socio-economic related issues	No specific issues
Product details	Pollack is sold in fillets, steaks or cutlets. Can be substituted for cod and haddock.
Season	May - September

Pouting

Common and scientific names	Pouting; Pout; Bib (*Trisopterus luscus*)
Species detail	A member of the cod family. Pouting is a very common fish in inshore waters, particularly in rocky areas where large schools form around wrecks and reefs. Can live on the outer shelf, but moves inshore to depths of 50m or less for spawning. Small pouting are very abundant in shallow water over sand. Spawns in March to April. Attains a size of 40-46cm, more usually 20-32 cm. Maximum reported age 4 years.
Species distribution	Eastern Atlantic: British Isles and Skaggerak to the Western African coast. Also in western Mediterranean.
Species and/ or stock status	Species not targeted commercially. No information available on stock status, species not assessed.
Method of capture	Generally line caught locally. Also as by-catch in inshore trawl and line fisheries.
Management	No management regime for this species. Non-quota species and no MLS specified.
Fishery and marine ecosystem related issues	No specific issues.
Health, welfare and socio-economic related issues	No specific issues
Product details	Eaten whole, gutted fresh or frozen.
Season	No information

Prawns (cold-water)

Common and scientific names	Prawn or northern prawn (northern or pink shrimp used interchangeably). *(Pandalus borealis).* Also known as crevette (a French term).
Species detail	Prawns are crustaceans belonging to the family *Pandalidae.* They are found on muddy sea-bottoms in depths from 10 – 500 m. They thrive in cold waters at temperatures between 2–8° C. *Pandalus* develops initially as a male then later becomes female during a 5-year life span. There is great variation in both the age (2-4 years) at which males change sex and therefore the number of males that become females. This enables individuals to maximise their reproductive success. When females mate their eggs or roe are carried under the lower part of the body where they stay until the larvae hatch. After spawning, in summer-autumn, females move into coastal waters where eggs hatch in winter. Juveniles remain inshore for about a year before migrating offshore as they begin to mature. Total adult length about 15 cm.
Species distribution	Main commercial stocks or fisheries in the north-east Arctic, Greenland, Norwegian, Icelandic waters and North Sea.
Species and/ or stock status	Important commercial species widespread throughout boreal waters in the North Atlantic and Pacific and Arctic Oceans. *Pandalus* is the main cold-water prawn landed and imported into the UK. The state of many stocks is generally unknown – catches have doubled in some areas in recent years. Stock in northern North Sea considered to be within safe biological limits, though spawning stock biomass is poorly estimated. Stocks are known to fluctuate due to environmental factors such as temperature and predation. As with most short-lived species fisheries are highly dependent on year class strength i.e. the breeding success of the population in any given year.
Method of capture	Trawling – bottom pair trawling (2 boats) or twin or multi-rig otter trawling (one boat). Usually in depths of up to 400 m depending on area fished. Mesh sizes are small at about 35mm. Also taken in traps. Trapping reduces disturbance of seabed and by-catch and produces a better quality catch.
Management	Fishing controlled by TAC in EU waters. NAFO also has responsibility for stock management. Measures also taken nationally for management of stocks e.g. closed seasons.
Fishery and marine ecosystem related issues	By-catch of non-target fish species - sorting grids are compulsorily fitted in nets in Norwegian, Canadian and US waters to reduce by-catch; prawn is an important prey for several fish species especially cod; egg-bearing females are frequently taken in the fishery and the eggs removed in processing; biology affected by temperature and climate change.
Health, welfare and socio-economic related issues	Prawns are an excellent source of vitamin B12 and are rich in soluble Vitamin A,E and D.
Product details	Sold whole, usually peeled, boiled and frozen. Used in prawn cocktails, sandwiches etc.
Season	All year

Red Mullet

Common and scientific names	Red mullet or goatfish *(Mullus surmuletus)*
Species detail	Red mullet – no relation to grey mullet – belong to the *Mullidae* family. In the Mediterranean it spawns in summer. It can attain a maximum length of 45 cm and a weight of 1 kg. Red mullet is reported to live up to 10 years. They have two long barbels – sensory organs – with which they probe for food in the sea bed. This is the reason for their alternative name – goat fish.
Species distribution	*Mullidae* are distributed throughout the world in tropical and warm temperate seas. Around 60 species are known. Only one species - *Mullus surmuletus* – is found in northern European seas where it is scarce. In summertime, however, during its northerly migration it is found in warmer waters off the south coast of England, English Channel and southern North Sea.
Species and/ or stock status	No information available, species not assessed.
Method of capture	No directed fisheries. Occasional landings are made off English Channel coasts. Probably taken as by-catch in trawl fisheries. Taken occasionally by anglers.
Management	Not managed in northern European waters.
Fishery and marine ecosystem related issues	No specific issues
Health, welfare and socio-economic related issues	Although red mullet is regarded as a white fish it has a slightly higher fat content than most other species with similar flesh. Red mullet must be eaten fresh as it is usually sold ungutted.
Product details	Sold and cooked ungutted. Red mullet are best eaten grilled, fried or baked. The innards particularly the liver is considered a delicacy and has a very high value.
Season	May - November

Salmon

Common and scientific names	Salmon or Atlantic salmon *(Salmo salar)*
Species detail	The Atlantic salmon is one of 4 species of salmonids indigenous to European waters. It occupies freshwater, brackish and marine waters during its lifecycle. Salmon spawn in rivers in fresh water in November and December. Eggs are laid in nests in the gravel beds of rivers called 'redds'. Eggs hatch in April to May. After hatching they are referred to as alevins. After 3-4 weeks the young fish or parr emerge from the gravel to feed. They may spend up to 2-3 years in the river before migrating to sea as smolts. Entry to the sea occurs between March and June. They remain at sea, during which time they may migrate long distances to Norway and west Greenland to feed, for 1-4 years before returning to their natal rivers to spawn. Many die after spawning but some survive to spawn a 2nd or 3rd time. Adult salmon can attain a length of 150 cm and weight of 36-45 kg. Max recorded age is 13 years. The Pacific salmon *(Oncorhynchus spp.)* are shorter lived species (max. 7 years) and much more prolific breeders than Atlantic salmon. Pacific salmon always die after spawning.
Species distribution	Species distributed throughout north-east and north-west Atlantic, ranging from south-west Greenland and Northern Labrador to the Mediterranean. Landlocked populations are found in Russia, Finland, Sweden and North America.
Species and/ or stock status	Wild Atlantic salmon are threatened by overfishing – driftnets and traps take large numbers of fish as they return to rivers to spawn; pollution; climate change; and dams. Stocks of wild Atlantic salmon have been halved in the last 20 years disappearing from 309 of 2000 traditional breeding areas world-wide. 90% of the known healthy populations exist in only 4 countries – Norway, Iceland, Ireland and Scotland.
Method of capture	Mainly netted in gill and trammel nets or in traps. Also popular game or recreational sport fish. Species widely farmed.
Management	Wild stocks managed by North Atlantic Salmon Conservation Organisation (NASCO) (see Chapter 6); salmon farming subject to EU and UK legislation (see Chapter 5); closed season for game fishing from November to February; Alaskan salmon fishery certified as an environmentally responsible fishery by the Marine Stewardship Council.
Fishery and marine ecosystem related issues	Stock depletion and virtual extinction of wild Atlantic salmon; issues relating to farming of salmon (see Chapter 5) such as discharge of nutrients and other effluent; impact of parasites (sea-lice) found on farmed fish on wild salmon stocks; impact of escapees from farms on genetics of wild fish; impact on other fisheries e.g. shell fisheries; industrial fishing - use of wild-caught fish for salmon feed.
Health, welfare and socio-economic related issues	Salmon is an oily fish rich in Omega 3. It is also a good source of Vitamin D, phosphorus and calcium; recent reports of high levels of PCBs and dioxins in farmed salmon due to bioaccumulation of toxins in feed (fish meal).
Product details	Sold fresh, whole, sliced or as cutlets or fillets, frozen, canned, pickled (gravadlax) or smoked. Eaten: steamed, fried, roasted, broiled and baked. Pacific salmon in particular Pink salmon *(O. gorbuscha)* and red or sockeye salmon *(O. neka)* is used in canned products. Salmon used as substitute for sushi and in sashimi. Eggs used to produce caviar. Marine Stewardship Council certified Alaskan salmon widely available. Organic salmon increasingly available in UK.
Season	Farmed: All year; wild Atlantic salmon: April to September

Sandeel

Common and scientific names	Sandeel, sandlance (US) *(Ammodytes marinus)*
Species detail	Sandeel is an extremely common offshore species and is not usually found in water less than 30m. It is a short-lived species, living no longer than 7-8 years, although fishing has reduced life expectancy to less than 2 years. Spawning takes place in winter, from January to March. It remains buried in the substrate (sandeels prefer coarse sand) of the seabed for much of the day and during the over-wintering phase from September to March. It is only available in the water column and surface waters in the summer months. Although *A.marinus* is one of 5 species of sandeel found in British waters it is this species that forms the basis of the industrial sandeel fishery in the North Sea.
Species distribution	Widespread and abundant offshore species. Numerically sandeels are the most abundant fish in the North sea.
Species and/ or stock status	Stocks of important commercial interest in North Sea, Shetland, Western Isles and off the north west Scottish coast. Generally considered to be within safe biological limits. However industrial fishing boats have been unable to fill their quota in the North Sea in recent years.
Method of capture	Mid-water trawl. Mesh size can be as small as 16 mm.
Management	Managed by TAC in North Sea - currently set at in excess of 1,000,000 tonnes. Fishery closely monitored in Shetland waters after stock collapse and poor breeding success of sea-birds which prey on sandeel and deaths of 1,000s of chicks from starvation in 1980s. Industrial fishing is currently restricted in areas in close proximity to sea-bird colonies in the North Sea e.g. Wee Bankie off Firth of Forth, Scotland, during the breeding season.
Fishery and marine ecosystem related issues	Ecological impacts associated with removal of vast quantities of biomass at the base of the food chain; sandeel is a major prey species for seabirds, seals, fish (cod, saithe, haddock, whiting etc.) and cetaceans; reduced breeding success in marine birds, kittiwake and puffin in particular, attributed to over-fishing of sandeel stocks particularly in areas close to breeding colonies; by-catch of fish generally immature species of commercial interest.
Health, welfare and socio-economic related issues	No specific issues
Product details	Primarily targeted by industrial fisheries for reduction to fishmeal and oil. Used in the manufacture of animal feed (poultry, pig and fish) and for human consumption in products such as margerine. Also used as fertilizer and at one time as fuel. Used by anglers for bait. May also be sold for human consumption as whitebait.
Season	April - August

Scallop

Common and scientific names	Scallop or King scallop *(Pecten maximus)*
Species detail	Scallops are bivalve molluscs found on sand and gravel in a range of depths from shallow waters in sea lochs to shelf waters over 100m. They have two shells or valves. The upper valve is flat and the under one or right valve, cupped shape. Scallops always rest on the right valve in order to maintain balance. Scallops begin life attached by byssus threads (a glue like substance) to rocks or substrate then become free swimming in later life. They live in the seabed partially buried in sands and gravels. Scallops are hermaphrodites (i.e. both male and female) and become fully mature at about 3 years old. Most spawning occurs in the warmer months from April to September. Scallops can grow to 15 cm in diameter, weighing in excess of 350 g, and may live 20 years or more. Age can be calculated by the growth rings on the upper valve.
Species distribution	Distributed widely throughout Atlantic waters from Norway to the Iberian Peninsula. King scallop is fished extensively in British waters. Main fishing areas in British waters are: English Channel; Irish Sea (Isle of Man); west of Scotland; and the Moray Firth (Scotland).
Species and/ or stock status	No specific information available. In response to increasing demand and unpredictable supply from the wild, scallops are now widely cultivated or farmed.
Method of capture	King scallops are fished all around the coast – the most widespread method of fishing is dredging. Also hand-picked by divers (method restricted by depth to 5-20 m). Scallops also widely farmed. Since the 1970s a valuable fishery for the smaller Queen scallop *Chlamys opercularis* has existed. 'Queenies' are harvested in the same way as scallops, and by modified traps.
Management	EU MLS for King scallops is 100 mm or 110 mm in Irish Sea. MLS for Queen scallops is 40mm. Also managed by Several and Regulating Orders (see Chapter 5). Isle of Man fishery closed from June to October.
Fishery and marine ecosystem related issues	Dredging damages the sea-bed – diver caught scallops are generally larger and of better quality and cause minimal damage to the environment. Also access is restricted by depth which creates a 'refuge' for natural populations; removal of undersized animals; removal of wild spat (young scallop) from the wild for cultivation purposes. Although spat is now widely produced in commercial hatcheries.
Health, welfare and socio-economic related issues	Scallops are filter feeders and can accumulate toxins in their flesh. However, water quality standards for shellfish (bivalve & gastropod molluscs) for human consumption is controlled and may only be harvested commercially from designated shellfish growing areas. Fishing for scallops recently banned in Scotland because of ASP – Amnesic Shellfish Poisoning – caused by a toxic algal bloom occurring along the coast during warmer months; scallops cooked alive.
Product details	Scallop meat (can be bought alive in its shell) comprises the white adductor muscle (which it uses to open and close its shell) and the orange (female) and creamy (male) roe. In Classic times the scallop shell was worn as a badge by pilgrims visiting the shrine of St James!
Season	September – March

Seabass

Common and scientific names	Bass; European seabass; sea perch; or sea wolf *(Dicentrarchus labrax)*
Species detail	Seabass belongs to a family of spiny-finned fish called *Moronidae*, closely related to the *Serranidae* or groupers. Adult bass live both offshore and inshore and in estuaries, sometimes entering freshwater during summer, but are generally found in deeper, warmer water offshore during winter. Often found in close proximity to reefs, wrecks and sandbanks. Bass breeds from March to mid-June, mostly in April, near the British Isles in offshore waters. The earliest and most prolific spawning occurs in deep offshore waters, mostly in the western English Channel. Larvae hatch and juveniles remain in sheltered habitats for 4-6 years, before adopting the migratory movements of adults. It is a long lived species, which may exceed 25 years and achieve a length of up to 100 cm with max weight of 12 kg. Nowadays fish exceeding 55 cm (2 kg) are becoming rare. Males are sexually mature at 36-38 cm at approx. 5 years old and females at 42-45 cm when they are approx. 6 years old.
Species distribution	East Atlantic: Norway to Morocco; Canaries and Senegal; including Mediterranean and Black Sea; North Sea; Baltic Sea; English Channel. A relatively common fish in the sea around England and Wales, Ireland and the southern North Sea coasts; it becomes much rarer to the north but has been extending its distribution north in recent years due to an increase in sea temperature around the UK.
Species and/ or stock status	Valuable recreational and commercial species. Commercial exploitation has escalated in recent years decimating numbers of mature wild fish. Stocks increasingly dependent on first-time spawners. Seabass has benefited from warmer waters around the UK.
Method of capture	Taken by gill-nets and rod and line in inshore waters and by pelagic mid-water trawlers in winter off-shore fishery. Also by sport anglers with rod and line and by sport divers with spearguns. Species is now widely farmed in the Mediterranean.
Management	Juveniles are protected by EU MLS (36 cm), nursery areas and gillnet mesh controls. National legislation restricts boat fishing for bass in nursery areas. Recreational angling subject to size limits and/or 'bag' limits and seasonal controls. 'Catch and release' is becoming more widespread in angling as stocks and individual sizes decline. Research indicates that approx. 75% of bass captured by UK sport anglers are returned alive.
Fishery and marine ecosystem related issues	By-catch of marine mammals in mid-water and pelagic trawls; winter fishery targets spawning and pre-spawning fish; exploitation of juveniles in bass nursery areas; bass also threatened by barrages, marinas and pollution in European and UK waters.
Health, welfare and socio-economic related issues	Due to competition from commercial fisheries the socio-economic benefits derived from angling have declined. The value of recreational use is reported to exceed that of commercial UK landings by 5-7 times.
Product details	Sea bass is popular in the restaurant trade. Sold fresh, whole or as steaks, cutlets or fillets. May be baked, grilled, steamed or roasted. Also particularly popular in Chinese cooking. Small high quality farmed bass (clearly labelled as such) is widely available.
Season	August – March. Farmed fish are available all year around.

Shark

Common and scientific names	Shark (Various species - see below for details)
Species detail	Sharks, rays and the rarely encountered chimaeras are collectively called elasmobranchs and are distinguished from bony fish (teleosts) by their cartilagenous skeletons. In particular they are distinguished from bony fish in the way that they reproduce. All sharks have internal fertilization. Worls-wide there are between 380 and 480 species of shark. Depending on species, sharks are thought to live for between 25 and 200 years. Compared to human 5 senses, sharks have 7. In addition to our 5 senses sharks can detect vibrations in the water and have a unique bio-electrical system used to detect and home in on the weak electrical fields produced by living animals. Species widely available for consumption in the UK are dogfish (see p*) and pelagic sharks such as tope (*Galeorhinus galeus*), mako (*Isurus oxyrinchus*) and porbeagle (*Lamna nasus*). Pelagic sharks are distinct from deep-water squalid sharks such as leafscale gulper and Portuguese dogfish or siki which are taken in deep-water fisheries and are largely retained for their liver-oil.
Species distribution	Sharks are wide ranging and found world-wide.
Species and/ or stock status	World-wide, sharks are being removed from our seas at an alarming rate - over 730,000 tonnes landed every year, directly threatening their long-term survival. Indirectly, global warming, habitat change, coastal development, and pollution also affect shark populations. Tope is assessed as Vulnerable by IUCN. They are particularly long-lived and slow to mature. The global population has been significantly reduced over the last 60 years. Although wide-ranging and having a relatively fast growth rate mako has a low reproductive capacity and is vulnerable to exploitation. Mako is asessed as at Lower Risk (close to meeting the threatened thresholds) by IUCN. The North Atlantic population of porbeagle has been seriously over-exploited in long-line fisheries. Porbeagle is assessed as Vulnerable by IUCN.
Method of capture	Long-line and gill-nets.
Management	Shark fisheries are not regulated under the CFP. The Food and Agriculture (FAO) Plan of Action for the Conservation and Management of Sharks (1998) provides guidance for countries wishing to set up shark fisheries management programmes.
Fishery and marine ecosystem related issues	Overfishing and stock collapse - world-wide an estimated 100 million sharks are killed each year; sharks are vulnerable to exploitation because they are slow growing with low reproductive rates; shark-finning; by-catch of marine turtles, mammals and other endangered species in targeted fisheries for sharks; by-catch of sharks in fisheries for species such as tuna and swordfish (in 1993 82,000 blue sharks were taken as by-catch by the French and Spanish tuna fishery alone).
Health, welfare and socio-economic related issues	Shark-fin soup widely eaten in the Far East. Also sizeable markets for shark fin in Europe and US. Fins may fetch over £30 per kilo. Blue sharks and other oceanic species are the preferred species taken. Because of its high value, its consumption is associated with status. Shark-fin soup is often served to impress and/or influence business clients. Shark liver oil capsules have alleged benefits for ADD.
Product details	Shark meat sold skinned as steaks; fins used in making soup; liver oil used in manufacture of health products also used for cosmetics and recently as a lubricant in the aviation industry; shark battered and sold deep-fried in fish and chip shops as 'flake'; skin used as leather - once used as sandpaper called 'shagreen'.
Season	All year

Shrimp (cold-water)

Common and scientific names	Shrimp, common shrimp or brown shrimp (*Crangon vulgaris*)
Species detail	Crangon is found mainly in shallow water around the British coast. It grows to about 8 cm and can live for about 3-4 years.
Species distribution	Distributed throughout Mediterranean, Atlantic, English Channel, North Sea and Baltic. Crangon spp. constitute the majority of landings of cold-water shrimps. Majority of shrimp marketed in UK comes from fishing grounds off the south-east coast and Morecambe Bay in the north-west.
Species and/ or stock status	No international or national assessment of shrimp stocks, only ad hoc investigations to evaluate the interaction between shrimp fisheries and the environment.
Method of capture	Trawling
Management	EU minimum mesh size of 16 mm. Veil nets and separators used (often on a voluntary basis) to exclude juvenile fish from catch.
Fishery and marine ecosystem related issues	By-catch of non-target marine organisms.
Health, welfare and socio-economic related issues	UK shrimp industry small and specialized, providing local employment; shrimp boiled alive usually onboard the fishing vessel.
Product details	Shrimp are boiled and sold cooked and whole. Eaten fresh or frozen.
Season	No information

Skate

Common and scientific names	Skate or common skate *(Raja batis)*
Species detail	Skate belong to the *Rajidae* family which includes skates and rays. The common skate is the largest European batoid fish. Females can reach lengths of 285 cm and males 205 cm. It is a bottom-dwelling species usually found in shallow coastal waters and shelf seas to 200 m, but occasionally down to 600 m. Males mature at a length of 125 cm (over 10 years old). Size and age at maturity for females is unknown. Longevity is estimated at 50 years. Mature females can produce up to 40 large eggs per year, which are laid in the spring and summer in leathery puches called mermaids purses.
Species distribution	Common skate are found in the north-east Atlantic from Madeira and northern Morocco to Iceland and northern Norway. Tagging records indicate that the majority of fish spend their entire life within a relatively small coastal area.
Species and/ or stock status	The common skate belies its name as it is becoming very rare in UK shallow seas and in European waters. Once one of the most abundant rajids in the north-east Atlantic and Mediterranean, common skate is now endangered and extirpated from many areas. It has probably been fished to extinction in the Irish Sea and is extremely rare in the central and southern North Sea, the western Baltic and western Mediterranean. The IUCN Red List assessment for this species is Endangered.
Method of capture	Taken as by-catch in bottom trawl fisheries and in targeted fisheries using lines and set nets. Also targeted by anglers. As populations become more depleted in shelf seas, fisheries are moving into deeper water to exploit previously unfished populations.
Management	EU TAC for skate & ray (no distinction made between species) in the North Sea only. Some SFCs specify MLS within waters under their jurisdiction. The common skate is the subject of a Biodiversity Action Plan (BAP) (Chapter 6) which aims to stabilise populations by minimising fishing mortality and legally protect it in at least 5 key areas of abundance in UK waters. A number of organisations including the Shark Trust have responsibility for implementing the plan.
Fishery and marine ecosystem related issues	Skates are vulnerable to over-exploitation because of their low fecundity and high age at first maturity; over fishing of juveniles or immature fish and females, which are larger than males, leading to stock depletion and eventual collapse.
Health, welfare and socio-economic related issues	No specific issues
Product details	The edible part of the skate is the fins or 'wings' which are generally removed for sale and skinned. Eaten boiled, poached or fried.
Season	May - February

Snapper

Common and scientific names	Snapper *(Lutjanus spp.)*. Red snapper not to be confused with the cold-water Red fish *Sebastes* spp.
Species detail	Snappers belong to the Family *Lutjanidae* which includes over 200 species. They are bright coloured predatory shoaling fish. Adults are usually found amongst rocks and corals. Young inhabit shallow waters often in mangrove areas. They are generally large species from 80 to 160 cm length and 10 – 60 kg depending on species. Some are reasonably long-lived with reported ages of up to 16 years old.
Species distribution	Snappers are found world-wide in tropical and sub-tropical waters.
Species and/ or stock status	Many species of snapper are over-fished. The mutton snapper *Lutjanus analis* and the Cubera snapper *Lutjanus cyanopterus* are both assessed as Vulnerable by IUCN. Many other species are over-exploited locally e.g. Northern red snapper *L. campechanus*.
Method of capture	Longlines; handlines; pots; divers. Also popular game or recreational sport fish.
Management	No management framework in UK as it is an imported species (from US, Far East, and NZ etc.). Managed at national levels e.g. Northern red snapper closely protected in US waters where it has been heavily exploited; Fishery Management Plan to protect reef species such as mutton snapper in Puerto Rico and US Virgin Is. Plan prohibits fishing in the closed season; use of poisons and dynamite; taking of species for aquarium trade. Mesh sizes are also specified for traps.
Fishery and marine ecosystem related issues	Overfishing and stock depletion; by-catch of juvenile snappers in shrimp fisheries; by-catch of sharks and turtles on longlines; snappers exploited for aquarium trade; damage to reefs from boats and divers; use of irresponsible fishing methods including poison and dynamite which destroys reefs and their ecology; destruction of snappers habitat e.g. reefs and mangroves by mans activities.
Health, welfare and socio-economic related issues	Ciguatera poisoning. This is an illness caused by eating reef fish that have accumulated a poison called ciguatoxin. The poison gets into fish feeding on algae contaminated with the toxin. The poison can then accumulate in larger fish when they eat the reef fish, which is then eaten by man.
Product details	Snapper is available whole. Usually sold fresh as steaks, cutlets or fillets (skinned or unskinned). Eaten steamed, broiled or baked.
Season	All year

Spider Crab

Common and scientific names	Spider crab (Maia squinado)
Species detail	The spider crab is the largest crab found in British waters with a carapace width of up to 200mm. They have a triangular-shaped body which is covered with spines and bristles. Female crabs become berried (egg-bearing) from April onwards. By June all mature females are berried. The hatching period extends from July until November. Some females produce two batches of eggs in a season. Larvae have a relatively short duration of pelagic life of 2 weeks. Juveniles remain in shallow (less than 20 m) coastal waters until reaching maturity in their second year. As with all crabs, spider crabs moult their shells in order to grow. As they attain maturity, both male and females moult for the last time, when their carapace (shell) width ranges from 85-200 mm for males and 70-175 mm for females. Recaptures of tagged mature spider crabs suggest that they make seasonal migrations into deeper water (over 50m) from September to January returning again to shallow water from April to June.
Species distribution	Spider crabs are distributed in the east Atlantic from northern Scotland south to Guinea. They are present in the southern North Sea, the Irish Sea, the Channel and most parts of the Mediterranean, but are absent from the Baltic and Black Seas. In the English Channel, spider crabs are most abundant in the western Channel, particularly in the areas from Cap de la Hague to Guernsey and to Morlaix.
Species and/or stock status	No information on stock status, though the fishery in the eastern Channel is less important than that in the western Channel.
Method of capture	Tangle nets.
Management	EU MLS of 120 mm (maximum body width) specified for this species.
Fishery and marine ecosystem related issues	Over-fishing of local populations; use of mono-filament net which may be lost resulting in 'ghost fishing'.
Health, welfare and socio-economic related issues	No specific issues
Product details	Eaten cooked and whole or meat removed from shell.
Season	April - October

Sprat

Common and scientific names	Sprat *(Sprattus sprattus)*
Species detail	Sprat is one of the smaller members of the herring family. It can attain a maximum length of about 16 cm and becomes sexually mature at 13-14 cm at an age of 2 years. Lives for about 6 years. Sprats spawn in the spring and summer. The eggs and larvae are planktonic and drift inshore as they develop. Juveniles i.e. those in their first year are frequently found in inshore coastal waters. In summer sprats are found in depths of 10 – 50 m but move into deeper water in the winter.
Species distribution	Distributed throughout noth-east Atlantic (from the North Sea to Baltic south to Morocco). Also Mediterranean, Adriatic and Black Sea. Important fisheries occur in the Skagerrak & Kattegat; the Baltic; Norwegian waters; and North Sea.
Species and/ or stock status	No specific information available. No significant reductions to TACs made in 2001. Generally levels of fishing effort were maintained which suggests that these stocks are not yet overfished.
Method of capture	Sprat is taken in purse seine and mid-water trawl nets using small meshes in the size range 16 mm (minimum allowed) to 99 mm. In Norway sprat is driven up fjords by nets and penned until needed by canning factories.
Management	Sprat is managed as an industrial species in EU waters. Other industrial species i.e. those fished for indirect human consumption are blue whiting, Norway pout, sandeel (p.85) and capelin. A TAC is specified for sprat in EU waters.
Fishery and marine ecosystem related issues	Ecological impacts associated with removal of vast quantities of biomass at the base of the food chain; sprat is a prey species for seabirds, seals, fish (cod, saithe, haddock, bass etc.) and cetaceans; by-catch of fish generally immature species of commercial interest; fishing of immature sprat in fisheries for whitebait; by-catch of marine mammals in large purse-seine and mid-water trawl nets.
Health, welfare and socio-economic related issues	Oily fish rich in Omega 3. Small bones are a good source of calcium.
Product details	Young sprats (in their first year) are sold as whitebait for human consumption. Sprats are often baked or roasted in the same way as sardines. Popular in Scandanavia where they are smoked and canned (brislings). Also targeted by industrial fisheries for reduction to fishmeal and oil, used in the manufacture of animal feed (including mink), and fertilizer. Also used as bait by anglers.
Season	October – March

Squid

Common and scientific names	Squid, common or veined squid *(Loligo forbesi)*. Various species also known as calamari from the Italian name.
Species detail	Squid is a cephalopod belonging to the same group or class as cuttlefish and octopus. Atlantic squid is a member of the *Loliginidae* family. Squid retain an internal shell or pen and are characterised by a large, fleshy body or mantle. Most species are highly mobile and rapid movement is obtained by jet propulsion. A squid can move forward to attack and backwards for escape. It is an annual species having a one year life-cycle with a single breeding season from December to May throughout its range. After mating both males and females die.
Species distribution	Cephalopod molluscs occur in all oceans of the world and occupy all the main zones of the sea. *L. Forbesi* is widespread throughout the north-east Atlantic and the Mediterranean in subtropical and temperate waters and is the basis of many commercially important fisheries e.g. Azores. Two families of squid are extensively exploited the *Loliginidae* in the Atlantic and the *Omnastrephidae* in the Pacific.
Species and/ or stock status	No specific information available. The significance of cephalopod stocks to international commercial fisheries is of recent, but growing importance. Fisheries in UK waters (mostly Scottish waters) tend to be small and non-targeted, squid being generally taken as by-catch.
Method of capture	Main methods are trawling and 'jigging'. Squid also appears as by-catch in whitefish and Nephrop trawl fisheries.
Management	No specific management regime. Non TAC or quota species.
Fishery and marine ecosystem related issues	Cephalopods play an important part in oceanic and coastal food webs. Squid is an important prey species for marine mammals – removal of large quantities of species at the base of the food chain - ' fishing down marine food webs' - has potential consequences for the marine ecosystem and the species that rely on them for food; squid is captured before it has a chance to spawn; discarding of squid taken as by-catch early in a fishing trip.
Health, welfare and socio-economic related issues	No specific issues
Product details	Squid are available fresh and frozen, whole and ungutted or ready prepared for cooking. Squid is best cooked quickly by either grilling, poaching or flash-frying it or slowly cooking it by stewing or braising. Squid or calamari is popular in the Mediterranean and other areas. Baby squid are sold as moscardini.
Season	May – October

Sturgeon

Common and scientific names	Sturgeon (various- see below for details)
Species detail	Sturgeon belong to a primitive family of fish known as *Acipenseridae*. They are confined to the rivers and seas of the temperate northern hemisphere; some live entirely in fresh water but most are anadromous, migrating into rivers to spawn. Sexual maturity in the Beluga *(Huso huso)* sturgeon is attained at 14 in males and 18 in females, most of this time being spent in the sea. They enter rivers in winter to spawn in the spring. Records exist of specimens (usually females) weighing 1.2 tonnes!
Species distribution	Sturgeons have a wide range in the Northern Hemisphere and are found in the Atlantic, north- east Asia, and Black and Caspian seas. Sturgeons of the Caspian Sea produce what is claimed to be the highest quality caviar and are the source of more than 90% of the world caviar trade.
Species and/ or stock status	Sturgeons the world over are now greatly depleted in numbers. Many of the 27 species – prized for their meat and eggs (caviar) – are in rapid decline. At one time sturgeons such as the Baltic sturgeon *(Acipenser sturio)* were vagrant visitors to British rivers, usually in May and June. Since the mid-1970s very marked declines in the populations of all 6 of the Caspian Sea's sturgeon species have been noted, especially Beluga, Russian *(A. gueldenstaedtii)* and stellate *(A. stellatus)* sturgeons. 5 of the 6 species of Caspian Sea sturgeons are assessed as Endangered by IUCN. In 2000, Russia exported 40 tonnes of black caviar, down 60% from 1999.
Method of capture	Nets. Sturgeon is now farmed in the Caspian Sea, the Mediterranean and south-west France.
Management	The trade in sturgeon eggs and meat is covered under the provisions of CITES - the Convention on International Trade in Endangered Species of Wild Fauna and Flora. All species are listed in Appendix II. The short-nosed *(A. brevirostrum)*, Dabrys *(A. dabryanus)* and Baltic sturgeon is Appendix I listed.
Fishery and marine ecosystem related issues	Sturgeons are vulnerable to over-exploitation because they are generally long-lived and slow to mature and depend on large rivers to spawn. Overfishing has caused the near extinction of many species. Sturgeon are also threatened by habitat degradation, hydro-electric dams and pollution.
Health, welfare and socio-economic related issues	Illegal trade in caviar. Poaching specifically by Mafia type gangs from the Caspian sea where 1 kg of top-quality caviar can fetch £2,000. The fish is stunned and the eggs removed whilst it is alive. Fish are then dumped.
Product details	Most notably their eggs – sold as caviar questionably the ultimate luxury food. The Rolls-Royce of caviar are the eggs of the largest sturgeon - the Beluga. Farmed caviar now widely available. There are also many caviar substitutes such as lumpfish and salmon roe and a vegetarian variety produced by Caviart www.finlaysfoods.co.uk (see Appendix 1).
Season	All year

Swordfish

Common and scientific names	Swordfish (*Xiphias gladius*)
Species detail	Swordfish is the only member of the Family *Xiphiidae*. They are ferocious predators and may use their swords to stun their prey (fish, crustacean and squid). It is a highly migratory species moving towards temperate or cold waters in summer to feed and returning to warmer waters to spawn. Females mature at 5-6 years at a length of 150-170 cm. They lay between 2 to 5 million eggs. Spawning reaches a peak between April to September in the Atlantic and occurs in spring and summer in the Pacific. In equatorial waters it occurs all year round. The best known spawning ground for this species is the Mediterranean where the most intense spawning takes place in July and August. Usually solitary it forms large schools during spawning. Swordfish live at the surface and as deep as 600 m. They can attain a maximum size of 4.5 m and a weight of 650 kg. Most swordfish over 140 kg are female.
Species distribution	Swordfish are wide-ranging solitary animals found throughout tropical, temperate and sometimes cold waters of the Atlantic, Indian and Pacific Oceans.
Species and/ or stock status	All three oceans have major swordfish fisheries. Western Europe, USA and Japan constitute almost 90% of the market. Atlantic populations of swordfish have fallen markedly since 1980 and are still in decline. Breeding populations have been reduced by more than 50% in the last 20 years. In the Pacific 8 nations take swordfish on a commercial scale with Japan accounting for more than two thirds of the catch. Status of Pacific swordfish is unknown. Because of massive increases in catches and fishing effort in Indean Ocean fishery is considered to be unsustainable. North Atlantic stock is assessed as Vulnerable by IUCN.
Method of capture	Long-line fisheries in the Western-Atlantic (US & Canada); harpoon, long-line & gill-net fisheries in Mediterranean (Italy, Greece & Spain) and long-lining off South America. Also taken as by-catch in drift-nets for tuna. Popular game or sport fish.
Management	ICCAT has responsibility for monitoring and managing swordfish populations. It has recommended a reduction in fishing effort as it is currently far above sustainable levels. Indian Ocean Stocks are managed by the Indian Ocean Tuna Commission. Pacific Stocks are largely unmanaged.
Fishery and marine ecosystem related issues	Over-fishing and stock depletion; over-fishing of juveniles – the average size of swordfish caught on long-lines has fallen from 120 kg 20 years ago to 30 kg today; by-catch of juveniles in long-line fisheries for tuna; by-catch of endangered species e.g. turtles, sharks, billfish in long-line fisheries.
Health, welfare and socio-economic related issues	Concern for human health posed by mercury levels in swordfish; in response to declining numbers, US Chefs took swordfish off the menu recently in support of a campaign organised by the Audubon Society to 'Give Swordfish A Break'.
Product details	Sold fresh or frozen cut into steaks. Also made into sashimi and teri-yaki (Japan - marinated in soy and grilled). Species similar in appearance (marlin, spearfish, sailfish (closely related) and paddlefish) are sometimes sold as swordfish.
Season	All year

Thornback ray

Common and scientific names	Thornback ray or roker (*Raja clavata*). Also called skate.
Species detail	Roker belongs to the *Rajidae* family which include skates and rays. Rajidae are cartilagenous species belonging to the same group as sharks and dogfish. In the spring the mature females move into inshore waters, followed within a month or so by mature males. Adults mate – fertilizaton of eggs is internal – for a second time before segregating into unisex schools. Egg-capsules are laid in shallow water from March to August. Eggs hatch 16-20 weeks later. The thornback ray can grow to a maximum length of 85 cm, width of 61 cm and 18 kg in weight. The largest specimens are always females.
Species distribution	Distributed throughout the Eastern Atlantic including the Mediterranean.
Species and/ or stock status	Although once one of the most abundant rajiids in the north-eastern Atlantic and Mediterranean commercial exploitation has reduced the abundance of this species in much of its natural range. The thornback is assessed as at Lower Risk (close to meeting threatened thresholds) by IUCN.
Method of capture	Thornback ray forms an important component of mixed demersal fisheries and is routinely landed as 'skate' in inshore fisheries. Taken as by-catch in bottom trawl fisheries and in targeted fisheries using lines and set nets. Also targeted by anglers.
Management	TAC for skate and ray (no distinction made between species) in EC waters of North and Norwegian Seas. MLS enforced in some inshore (within 6 miles) waters of UK e.g. South Wales Sea Fisheries Committee (SFC) specifies a MLS of 45 cm measured wingtip to wingtip for thornback ray. No EU MLS in force in waters outside 6 miles.
Fishery and marine ecosystem related issues	Rays are vulnerable to overexploitation because of their low fecundity and high age at first maturity; over-fishing of juveniles or immature fish and females, which are larger than males, leading to stock depletion and eventual collapse.
Health, welfare and socio-economic related issues	No specific issues
Product details	The edible part of the ray is the fins or 'wings' which are generally removed for sale and skinned. Eaten boiled, poached or fried.
Season	May - February

Tiger prawn (warm-water)

Common and scientific names	Black, Giant or Jumbo tiger prawn; Gambas; and Leader prawn (Penaeus monodon)
Species detail	The Tiger prawn belongs to the largest of the prawn and shrimp family the Penaeidae. Its lifecycle may be divided into 6 stages or phases from embryo to adult which it completes in one year. In the wild, spawning takes place in inshore or tidal waters in spring and autumn. As larvae mature it moves into deeper offshore waters. Females are larger than males. Males are sexually mature at around 37 mm carapace length and females at 47 mm. The age of sexual maturity varies from 5 to 11 months. Females produce about 250,000 - 800,000 eggs. Tiger prawns live up to 2 years in the wild - farmed prawns are usually harvested at 6 months. It can grow to 33 cm – although harvest size averages 20-28 cm. Its diet in the wild consists of crustaceans and molluscs.
Species distribution	Distributed over a huge range, from east and south-east Asia, through the Red Sea, Arabian Gulf, around Indian sub-continent, through Malay Archipelago to northern Australia and the Philippines. Most commonly farmed species in south-east Asia.
Species and/ or stock status	Tiger prawn is the most dominant single species from wild harvests, accounting for 6% of the world's landings of all shrimp and prawn. Throughout most of its range it represents less than 5% of the native prawn population.
Method of capture	Trawling – bottom pair trawling (2 boats) or twin or multi-rig otter trawling (one boat) in depths to 300 m. Also farming widespread. India and Indonesia account for much of the landings of wild-caught tiger prawns.
Management	Management subject to national jurisdiction and controls. Some countries and/or suppliers participate in multi-national management initiatives such as Global Aquaculture Alliance (GAA) (see Chapter 5).
Fishery and marine ecosystem related issues	Damage to sea bed and removal of biomass - large amounts of by-catch (35% of world's total), including endangered species such as turtles, are taken in trawl fisheries for penaeids (warm-water shrimp or prawns); habitat destruction specifically of coral reefs and mangroves – half the world's mangrove forests have been destroyed to create ponds for prawn and shrimp aquaculture; prawn farmers rely on wild stocks (broodstock) trawled in the wild for the production of larvae; Tiger prawn taken as by-catch in trawl fisheries for smaller Banana prawn (Penaeus merguiensis).
Health, welfare and socio-economic related issues	Some countries and/or suppliers participate in Ethical Trading Initiatives (ETI) (see Chapter 9) to promote environmental and ethical awareness; prawns often transported by air, dry packed, live in chilled sawdust. Animals can survive up to 24 hours and most are revived on reaching their destination.
Product details	Frozen whole and/or in blocks. Usually peeled and/or cooked as hors d'oeuvres. Also breaded, canned and dried. Also collected as bait in estuarine and coastal waters. A black spot (melanosis) on the shell indicates poor quality.
Season	All year

Trout

Common and scientific names	Trout - Sea trout or brown trout *(Salmo trutta)*; Rainbow trout *(Oncorhynchus mykiss)*.
Species detail	Both species belong to the salmon family *(salmonidae)*. Both are anadromous i.e. adapted to life in both fresh and sea water. Of the 2 species, rainbow trout is more widely farmed. *Salmo trutta* forms two basic types – the migratory or sea trout and the non-migratory or brown trout. *S. trutta* spawn in winter from October to January. The eggs are laid in nests in rivers known as 'redds'. *S. trutta matures* in 3-4 years. It can grow up to 140 cm and live up to 38 years. Its life history is similar to salmon. Rainbow trout is a non-indigenous species and more adapted to warmer waters. It reaches a maximum size of 120 cm and age of 11 years. Rainbows can grow to 20kg or more but sea trout seldom over 15 kg. Both species feed on crustaceans, insects and fish etc.
Species distribution	Both species are found where there is clean, well-oxygenated water, usually in lakes or streams in upland areas. Rainbow (introduced to Europe from the USA) and Brown trout (introduced to at least 40 countries including the USA in 1880, Australia and New Zealand, South Africa and South America) are widely introduced species with reports of adverse ecological impact after introduction. Only the brown trout is indigenous to the UK. Both species are widely cultivated and because of its popularity as a sport or game fish, brown trout is stocked to lakes and rivers. Brown trout also has the widest natural range of all salmonids.
Species and/ or stock status	Brown trout are threatened as a wild species in some areas, by habitat degradation and stocking of non-indigenous strains. Rainbow trout have very few self-sustaining or breeding populations in Europe, and are maintained chiefly by stocking with farmed fish.
Method of capture	Brown trout captured on lines by anglers. Both species widely farmed in UK.
Management	Fisheries for wild trout are tightly managed by licensing, closed seasons, gear restrictions and MLSs. Farming regulated by EU and UK Legislation (see Chapter 5).
Fishery and marine ecosystem related issues	Issues related to introduction of non-indigenous species such as hybridization and competition with and replacement of native species; issues related to farming of salmonids (see Chapter 5).
Health, welfare and socio-economic related issues	Salmonids are oily fish rich in omega 3
Product details	Eaten fresh and baked or grilled whole or as fillets. Rainbow trout also smoked.
Season	Farmed trout all year; wild brown trout April – September; wild Rainbow trout May – November.

Tuna

Common and scientific names	Tuna also called bonito or tunny. There are 6 commercially important species of tuna - Northern bluefin *(Thunnus thynnus)*, Southern bluefin *(T.maccoyii)*, Bigeye *(T. obesus)*, Yellowfin *(T.albacares)*, Skipjack *(Euthynnus or Katsuwonus pelamis)* and Albacore or long-fin tunny *(T. alalunga)*.
Species detail	Tuna belong to the Family *Scombridae*. They are large, oceanic fish and are seasonally migratory, some making trans-Atlantic journeys. Tuna feed on squid and also prey on schools of smaller fish, in particular herring, sprat, whiting, anchovy etc. Northern bluefin breeds in June in the Mediterranean and off Spain. Albacore spawns in May to June off the Portuguese and Spanish coasts. Tuna form mixed schools e.g. Albacore, skipjack, yellowfin and bluefin, often associated with floating objects. Tuna also school by size. Juveniles in particular are attracted to Fish Attraction Devices (FADs) used in their capture. They can reach ages of 10-25 years depending on species, although heavy fishing has reduced age expectancy considerably.
Species distribution	Tuna are found world-wide in cold, temperate and tropical seas.
Species and/ or stock status	Tuna is highly sought after and forms the basis of many fisheries word-wide. World catches have doubled in the last decade. The largest fisheries are in the South Pacific. Stocks are fully exploited with many overfished – global stocks of bluefin for example are at an all time low. Populations of Atlantic yellowfin are believed to have declined by 30% in the past 10 years (Yellow-fin comprise about 35% of world tuna catches) and concern is growing for Atlantic and Pacific populations of bigeye. Northern bluefin, Southern bluefin, bigeye and albacore tuna are listed by IUCN – Southern bluefin tuna is assessed as Critically Endangered.
Method of capture	Purse-seine; pole and line; longline; drift nets; trolling lines; and bait boats. Purse-seine (assessed by EII) and pole and line methods are 'dolphin friendly' – see Chapter 2 & 8. Tuna is 'farmed' in Japan, Australia and the Mediterranean. Juveniles are captured in the wild then fattened for market in sea cages or pens.
Management	ICCAT is responsible for the conservation of tunas and tuna-like species in the Atlantic and adjacent seas. The Commission for the Conservation of Southern bluefin Tuna (CCSBT) has specific interest in the management of Southern bluefin tuna.
Fishery and marine ecosystem related issues	By-catch of marine mammals in net fisheries - yellowfin is most commonly associated with dolphins taken as by-catch in many fisheries, particularly those in the Eastern Tropical Pacific (ETP); overfishing and stock depletion; discarding of immature tunas in purse-seine fisheries; by-catch of endangered species in long-line fisheries e.g. turtles, swordfish, marlin, sharks; illegal and over-quota fishing.
Health, welfare and socio-economic related issues	Tuna is an oily fish rich in Omega 3. This is however destroyed in the canning process; bluefin tuna is essentially a luxury food commodity and can sell for at least £30 for a tiny portion of the choicest cut - the toro or belly - in gourmet restaurants in Tokyo. Whole bluefins can fetch from £12 – £100,000 at Tokyo markets.
Product details	Tuna is sold fresh or frozen, usually as steaks or loins. Used in sushi (especially bluefin in Japan) and sashimi. Mainly canned (yellowfin and skipjack) in oil or brine for UK market. Wind-dried tuna (mojama) is popular in some parts of the Mediterranean. Liver of most types of tuna yields oil used in processing of leather.
Season	All year

Turbot

Common and scientific names	Turbot or European turbot *(Scophthalmus maximus)*
Species detail	Turbot belongs to a small family of left-eyed flat-fish *Scophthalmidae*. The family is confined to the North Atlantic basin and includes megrim and brill. Turbot is almost circular in shape. It lives in shallow inshore waters from the shoreline down to about 80 m over sandy and/or rocky bottoms. Young-of-the-year live in the surf zone. It spawns during spring and summer, between April and August, females each producing up to 10 million eggs. It can attain a length of 1 m and a weight of 25 kg. More usual lengths are 50-80 cm. Females are larger than males. Maximum reported age 26 years.
Species distribution	North-east Atlantic: throughout the Mediterranean, along European coasts to the Arctic Circle. Also found in most of the Baltic sea. Turbot, like brill, is close to the extremity of its range in northern European waters. Although rare in northern waters it is common in the southern North sea, English Channel and the Irish Sea.
Species and/ or stock status	No information available. It is a highly esteemed and valuable food fish and demand is high.
Method of capture	Caught in trawl and seine nets and by lines. Species is farmed in Norway, Portugal, Spain, France and UK.
Management	There is a TAC for this species in EU waters of the North Sea. TAC includes brill as no distinction is made between species. No MLS specified.
Fishery and marine ecosystem related issues	Overfishing – particularly of juveniles as there is no minimum landing size for this species; Turbot like brill is a warm-water fish – likely to become more widespread in northern waters as sea temperatures increase.
Health, welfare and socio-economic related issues	No specific issues
Product details	One of the most expensive fish – once a symbol of luxury and ostentation - it is mainly supplied to and sold by the restaurant trade. Turbot may be baked, grilled or poached. Farmed turbot available whole usually as 1-5 kg fish.
Season	April – February

Whelks

Common and scientific names	Whelk, common or European whelk *(Buccinum undatum)*. Also known as 'buckies'.
Species detail	Whelks are large marine gastropods or snails with strong, whitish or grubby shells. They are carnivorous scavengers and eat most things including oysters and scallops. Prey is detected at a considerable distance by smells carried in the water. Whelks are hermaphrodite – each individual producing eggs and sperm. They mate, however, exchanging sperm, so that eggs are cross-fertilised. Whelks breed during autumn and winter. Eggs are laid between November and January and hatch 3-9 months later. Eggs are contained in capsules – each capsule containing many hundreds of eggs. Several layers of capsules may be laid at a time to form a mass equivalent to their own size. Whelks may lay eggs together to form large, football size clumps. Only a few eggs are fertilised and hatch. Baby whelks emerge from the capsules in spring. Whelks are long-lived. Sexual maturity occurs at 5-7 years. Their shells can grow up to 11 cm and are often covered in barnacles. Empty shells are commandeered by hermit crabs.
Species distribution	Whelks are boreal species common in temperate seas. They are found on all coasts of the Atlantic from the tidal zone down to 200 m and are found all around Britain and on all types of sea bottom.
Species and/ or stock status	No specific information available. Fishing pressure has increased as fishermen seek new fishing opportunities to satisfy large and expanding export market to the Far East (South Korea).
Method of capture	Mostly caught in baited pots. Also dredged.
Management	A minimum landing size of 45 mm is specified for EU waters.
Fishery and marine ecosystem related issues	Whelks are affected by imposex – the formation of male sex organs in female gastropods – due to exposure to tributyltin (TBT) an anti-foulant paint used on ships hulls. This has the potential to affect breeding populations as normally an equal number of males and females is found. Use of TBT now banned; large-scale and often illegal removal of immature shore crabs for use as bait in commercial whelk fisheries.
Health, welfare and socio-economic related issues	Whelks are often the basis for small-scale coastal fisheries providing social-economic benefits for coastal communities.
Product details	Whelks are popular as a food in seaside towns. Sold at whelk stalls boiled in their shells on harvesting. Also used as bait. Whelk egg packets, called 'sea soap', used as a soap substitute.
Season	February – August

Whiting

Common and scientific names	Whiting or English whiting (*Merlangius merlangus*)
Species detail	It is a slender bodied sandy, blue-green coloured fish with conspicuous white sides and belly, silvery when alive. Length usually around 30-40cm. Up to 70 cm and 3 kg. Maximum reported age 20 years. A common fish in shallow inshore waters between 30 and 100 m. Feeds on shrimps, molluscs and small fish. Migrates to open sea after the first year of life. Young whiting found in association with medusae or jellyfish. The whiting also forms an important part of the diet of other, larger fishes and sea-birds.
Species distribution	North-east Atlantic: from the south-eastern Barents Sea and Iceland to Portugal, also in the Black Sea, Aegean Sea, Adriatic Sea and adjacent areas.
Species and/ or stock status	Important commercial fisheries in Norwegian and Faroese waters, northern North Sea and Irish Sea and Biscay. All stocks are assessed and all but the western Channel/Celtic Sea stock are outside safe biological limits.
Method of capture	Bottom otter trawl, seines and long-line.
Management	Species managed by system of TACs and Quotas and technical measures in EU waters. MLS 27cm (23cm in Skaggerak/Kattegat).
Fishery and marine ecosystem related issues	By-catch – whiting part of a complex mixed, demersal fishery including cod, haddock and saithe; discarding of immature cod, haddock etc.
Health, welfare and socio-economic related issues	Whiting is light and easily digestible and therefore a good choice for invalids and those on a low-fat diet.
Product details	Marketed fresh or frozen as whole fish or filleted. Also dried/salted and smoked. May be eaten steamed, broiled or baked.
Season	June - February

Winkle

Common and scientific names	Winkle or periwinkle (Littorina littorea)
Species detail	Winkles are gastropod molluscs. All species have distinct male and females. Shell size of up to 37 mm, but usually 25 mm. Lives from high water down to 40 m. During winter winkles migrate down towards or below the low water mark. Grazes on a range of micro and macroalgae. Females mature at 14 mm. Usually live 3 years but can survive for 4-5 years.
Species distribution	Widely distributed in coastal regions in the North Atlantic. They are distributed on all British coasts, though rare or absent in the Isles of Scilly and the Channel Isles. Nearly all commercial concentrations of winkle occur on large intertidal flats in lower reaches of estuaries.
Species and/ or stock status	No information available. Stocks vulnerable to local over-exploitation and depletion if fishery not controlled.
Method of capture	Tractor-towed harvesters; dredging – including use of back-pack vacuums; hand-picking or collection.
Management	May be managed by Sea Fishery Committee byelaws. Statutory Agencies also have an interest in the management of molluscs e.g. introduction of size limits.
Fishery and marine ecosystem related issues	Overexploitation by commercial harvesting – decreasing numbers and sizes at some beaches and estuaries; harvesting effects burrowing behaviour of winkles; removal of prey species for birds and other marine life; disturbance of seabed or mud and sand on beaches and in estuaries; grazing activity can be a major factor in structuring communities – removal of grazing animals such as winkles changes the structure of the community.
Health, welfare and socio-economic related issues	Winkles are grazers rather than filter-feeders and can concentrate toxins found in their food. A sample population of people eating locally-harvested cockles in Cumbria are being monitored for intake of plutonium.
Product details	Winkles are boiled, usually on harvesting. They are sold in their shells and the meat removed with a pin, then dipped in salt and vinegar, before eating.
Season	September – April

Witch

Common and scientific names	Witch (*Glyptocephalus cynoglossus*)
Species detail	Witch is a right-eyed flat fish belonging to the family *Pleuronectidae*. It is a moderately deep-water flat fish which lives on the lower continental shelf from 300 – 900 m and deeper. It spawns in summer. During the early stages of its life it floats in surface waters, moving to the sea-bed when it is 4-5 cm. Its growth is rather slow, sexual maturity is attained in 3-4 years. Witch may live for 14 years, but the maximum reported age is 25 years. Attains a maximum length of 55-60 cm (usually around 35 cm) and weight of 2-3 kg.
Species distribution	Atlantic: from northern Spain to northern Norway. Western Atlantic: Gulf of St. Lawerence and Grand Banks in Canada to North Carolina in USA.
Species and/ or stock status	No information available.
Method of capture	Mostly captured in trawls targeting whitefish or other flat fish species such as cod, plaice etc.
Management	Unprotected or non-pressure stock species in EU waters i.e. no TAC or technical conservation measures such as MLS.
Fishery and marine ecosystem related issues	No specific issues
Health, welfare and socio-economic related issues	No specific issues
Product details	Important as a food fish in northern Europe. Marketed whole, fresh or frozen
Season	May - February

Chapter Four

The Fishing Cycle

Introduction

Since prehistoric times, the living resources of the sea have provided mankind with an important source of food and employment. Shellfish, such as oysters and clams, have been gathered by hand from the earliest days of civilisation. Fish were more difficult to catch and required the development of suitable methods. Weirs, nets and traps were deployed from the shore before the development of boats permitted access to sheltered estuaries and coastal areas, and as boats and gear developed, fishermen later ventured into the open sea. By the 15th century, European fishing boats were working Icelandic grounds and less than 100 years later, the Newfoundland Banks in Canadian waters.

Food from the sea continues to grow in importance as efforts are made to maintain maximum resources to feed the world's increasing population. Today, fish and their products are traded globally and are the basis of an international trade in fishery commodities with an estimated value of US$53.4 billion in 1999.

World trade in fish

During the 1950s and 60s world marine and inland capture fisheries production increased on average by as much as 6% per year, trebling from 18 million tonnes (Mt) in 1950 to 56 Mt in 1969. Since then the average rate of increase has declined from 2% in the 1970s and 1980s to almost zero in the 1990s. In 1970, the limit of production for wild marine resources was predicted to be 100 Mt. By 2010 it is estimated that total demand for fish will reach 140 Mt of which 110 Mt will be for human consumption and 30 Mt for fishmeal. It is expected that demand will be satisfied by expansion in fish farming and exploitation of new fisheries, such as those found in deep-water.

> *Total world marine fisheries production in 1999 was estimated at 97.2 Mt of which 84.1 Mt (86.5%) was from capture fisheries and 13.1 Mt (13.5%) from aquaculture*
> *(Source FAO 2000)*

Where does fish come from?

The world's major fishing areas are located in the Atlantic, Pacific and Indian Oceans. The North-west Pacific had the largest reported catches in 1998 followed by the North-east Atlantic and the Western Central Pacific. The quantity of fish landed from these regions is determined by major productive stocks such as Atlantic herring in the North-east Atlantic, Alaska pollack and Japanese anchoveta in the North-west Pacific and skipjack and yellowfin tuna in the Western Central Pacific. Of the 84 Mt of fish caught in 1999, 62% was caught in the Pacific Ocean, 28% in the Atlantic and 10% in the Indian Ocean.

In 1998 the top fish exporting countries were China, Japan, USA, Russian Federation, Peru, Indonesia, Chile, and India. Together, these countries accounted for more than 50% of the total capture fisheries production in 1998. In 1999 China caught the largest quantity of fish - 15 Mt - and Peru had the second largest annual catch at 8.4 Mt. China has a population of more than 1.2 billion people, of which 1.9 million are engaged in capture fisheries. By 2005 fishery production in China is predicted to reach 46 Mt of which 65% will come from aquaculture.

Who eats fish?

About 75% of the world's catch is used for human consumption. The remainder is converted into fishmeal and oil used mainly in the manufacture of animal feeds. Asia is by far the most important fish-consuming region. Europe is the second largest fish-consuming continent and has the highest average per capita consumption of seafood. Healthy eating, lifestyle changes and recent scares about meat consumption are all contributing to diet change in European countries. The lowest levels of consumption occur in Africa and the Near East. Generally speaking, fish consumption is higher in developed countries than in developing countries, notable exceptions being small developing island states. Europe is the largest market for fish in the world and its fishing fleet is the largest fishing power after China and Japan.

Oyster trestles

The supply chain

The supply chain for fish involves firstly the catching of fish by the fishermen and fishing vessels at sea (the producers), followed by processing, marketing and distribution of the fresh, chilled or frozen products to processors, retailers, fish fryers, restaurateurs (the suppliers) and finally consumption by the public (the consumers).

> *World wide, 36 million people are engaged in fishing and fish farming. Less than half of these people - 15 million - work aboard fishing vessels many of which - 90% - are less than 24 metres in length*   *(Source FAO 2000).*

UK fishing industry

In 2001 the UK sea fish industry employed over 136,000 individuals in the various sectors. In Britain there are approximately 7,242 fishing boats (excluding those registered in the Channel Islands and Isle of Man) engaged in various fishing activities such as trawling, potting, netting, lining and dredging (see Table 1). Since 1970 the total number of regular fishermen in the UK has decreased from 17,480 to 12,970 in 1999. In the processing sector there are approximately 541 businesses employing 22,000 individuals. There are also some 1,400 fishmongers.

Red Mullet

Table 1: Main activity of the UK fishing fleet in 2000 (Source: DEFRA 2001)

Gear type	Number of boats	% of total	Registered tonnes	Power (kW)
Pelagic trawls	44	0.56	47,635	84,799
Beam trawl	111	1.42	23,927	90,556
Demersal, Seines & Nephrops trawls	1,208	15.45	111,437	355,914
Lines & nets	165	2.11	13,883	41,404
Shellfish: mobile	211	2.7	10,597	49,839
Shellfish: fixed	297	3.8	5,992	42,844
Distant water	13	0.17	17,331	26,895
Under 10 metres	5,769	73.77	20,247	288,386
Mussel dredgers	2	0.03	182	682
Total	7,820		251,231	981,319

Even though fishing contributes only 0.33% to the UK's and less than 1% to the European Union's Gross Domestic Product (GDP), it is of critical importance in such regions as Scotland, Northern Spain and France's Atlantic coast.

In 2000, some 748,000 tonnes of sea fish were landed into the UK by both the UK fleet and foreign vessels with a total value of £550 million. This compares with some 924,000 tonnes landed in 1998 with a value of £662 million (see Table 2).

John Dory

(Source: DEFRA 2001)

Year	1998		2000		
Landings by UK boats	Value (£M)	Tonnage (000 tonnes)	Value (£M)	Tonnage (000 tonnes)	% change (value; tonnage)
Into UK	484	553	422	464	-13% ; -16%
Abroad	178	371	128	284	-28% ; -23%
Total	662	924	550	748	-17% ; -19%

UK fishing ports and markets

The majority - 70% - of UK fishing interests are concentrated in Scotland. The largest fishing port (by value and live weight of landings) in the UK is Peterhead. Other significant Scottish ports are Lochinver, Fraserburgh and Aberdeen. The largest fishing ports in England are Newlyn (by value) and Plymouth (by weight). Milford Haven is the largest port in Wales. Whilst fish markets are commonly found in coastal areas, inland markets, such as Billingsgate in London, play an important role in the distribution of fish. Here hundreds of thousands of tonnes of fish from all over the UK and the rest of the world are marketed each year. Additionally manufacturers import significant quantities of fish directly from the supplying country or fishing vessels. One of the benefits of direct purchasing is 'traceablility'. Traceablility of fish is becoming increasingly important as retailers seek to market their fish as originating from 'responsibly' or 'sustainably' managed sources.

Fisheries

'Fisheries' is a general term used to denote all the activities concerned with the catching of living marine resources whether by line, net or other means. More specifically a fishery refers to the harvesting of one or more target species (with an associated by-catch of non-target species) within a given sea area. The populations of each species are composed of one or more 'stocks', each of which is exploited in a separate fishery area and may be biologically independent from other stocks of the same species. For example, for cod, notable stocks include the Arcto-Norwegian and North Sea stocks; and for herring, the Atlanto-Scandian stock is important.

Commercial fish are referred to in terms of pelagic and demersal (or ground fish). Pelagic species generally inhabit the surface to mid-water waters, examples are herring and mackerel, and demersal species such as cod and haddock are found closer to the seabed. Most invertebrate species such as molluscs and crustaceans (shellfish) live on or in the seabed and are part of the benthos (organisms inhabiting the seabed), but some like the squid, are pelagic.

Although there are some 22,000 – 25,000 species of fish in the world's oceans, only a small proportion are of commercial significance. In the North Sea, for example, there are some 224 species, but only 20 are of any commercial interest.

Fishing methods and gears

In the last 100 years, fishing has become increasingly technical and more efficient. Modern commercial fisheries are typically characterised by high capitalisation and investment in technology and equipment to improve, not only the efficiency of fishing operations, but also the safety and quality of working conditions at sea.

Main methods of fishing:

- seining
- trawling
- netting (e.g. drift and gill nets)
- hook and line

Worldwide, the most commercially important methods of fishing are purse seining and trawling. Purse seining is the principal method of fishing for pelagic species such as tuna, herring and mackerel for example, and trawling the principal method for demersal species such as cod, haddock, coley or saithe, plaice and sole.

Main types of fishing gears:

- encircling gears
- towed or dragged gears
- static gears
- traps

Trawls are the most important type of fishing gear used in the commercial fisheries of Northwest Europe, catching a greater weight of fish than any other method.

Fishing gear is also described in terms of mobile or active gears i.e. gears that are towed through the water, and static or passive gears i.e. those gears that are fixed to, or placed on, the seabed e.g. pots, fixed gill nets and traps.

Mobile: Towed or dragged gears

Examples of towed gears include otter trawls, beam trawls and dredges.

Otter trawl: The demersal or bottom trawl is a large cone-shaped net, which is towed across the seabed (see Figure 1). The forward part of the net - the 'wings' are kept open by otter boards or doors. Fish are herded between the boards and along the spreader wires or sweeps, into the mouth of the trawl where they swim until exhausted. They drift back through the funnel of the net, along the extension or lengthening piece and into the cod-end, where they are retained. Around the upper edge of the mouth of the net runs the headline (headrope or floatline) to which are fixed a number of floats; along the bottom of the mouth is the groundrope or footrope which is normally in contact with the seabed and is weighted.

Trawler

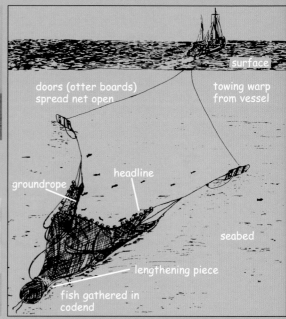

surface

doors (otter boards)
spread net open

towing warp
from vessel

headline

groundrope

seabed

lengthening piece

fish gathered in
codend

Beam trawler

Trawl gear

Depending on the depth of water fished and the way in which the gear is constructed and rigged, trawling may be used to catch different species. Trawls can be towed by one vessel using otter-boards as in bottom-trawling or by two vessels, each towing one warp, as in pair-trawling. Or more than one trawl can be towed simultaneously as in multi-rig trawling.

Multi-rigs are used widely for the capture of panaeid shrimps in tropical waters and more recently for Nephrops (langoustine or Dublin Bay prawns) and deep-water prawns in temperate waters. The speed at which the net is towed is important, varying with the swimming speed of the target species from about 1.5 to 5 knots for fast swimming fish.

In *mid-water pair trawling*, a method of fishing for pelagic species, such as seabass, mackerel and pilchards, the otter boards are replaced, and the mouth of the net kept open, by a pair of trawlers. This enables vast nets, often ¼ mile wide and ½ mile long, to be towed through the water column to capture the shoaling fish.

Beam trawl: In this type of trawl the mouth of the net is kept open by a beam which is mounted at each end on guides or skids which travel along the seabed. Beam trawlers are used to target flat fish species such as sole and plaice on or in the surface layers of sand. The trawls are adapted and made more effective by attaching tickler chains to the beam in front of the groundrope. These drag along the seabed in front of the net, disturbing the fish in the path of the trawl, causing them to rise from the sand and into the oncoming net. Electrified ticklers, which are less damaging to the seabed, have been developed but used only experimentally.

Table 3: Summary of main fishing gears and targeted species

MOBILE				FIXED	
Towed		Encircling		Static	
Gear	Species	Gear	Species	Gear	Species
Bottom trawl	Demersal e.g. cod, haddock, flatfish, monkfish	Purse seine	Pelagic e.g. tuna, mackerel, herring & sardines	Gill net	All roundfish, demersal & pelagic e.g. hake, etc
Bottom pair/ multi-rig trawling	Shrimp and prawn, also whitefish			Long-line (surface, bottom or vertical)	Various e.g. toothfish, tuna, swordfish, cod etc.
Mid-water trawl/pair-trawl	Seabass, hake, herring, mackerel, pilchards, squid & tuna	Seine net	Demersal e.g. haddock, cod & flatfishes Handline Mackerel, cod etc.	Pole & line	Tuna
Beam trawl	Flat fish e.g. sole & plaice			Pots or creels	Crustacea e.g. lobster, crab, octopus & Nephrops
Dredges	Molluscan shellfish e.g. scallops & oysters			Traps	Crustacea e.g. prawns

Dredging is used for harvesting bivalve molluscs such as oysters, clams and scallops from the seabed. A dredge is a metal framed basket with a bottom of connected iron rings or wire netting called a chain belly. The lower edge of the frame has a raking bar, with or without teeth, depending upon the species targeted. The catch is lifted off the seabed or out of the sea by the raking (or teeth) bar and passes back into the basket or bag.

Mobile: Encircling gears

Encircling gears, or seines are used throughout the world for the capture of pelagic fish such as herring, mackerel, pilchard, tuna and sprat in both coastal and ocean waters and for demersal species in some areas.

Purse seining: is the general name given to the method of encircling a school of fish on or near the surface with a large wall of net. The net is then drawn together underneath the fish (pursed) so that they are completely surrounded. It is one of the most aggressive methods of fishing and aims to capture large, dense shoals of mobile fish such as tuna, mackerel and herring.

Mussel dredger

Seine netting: is a bottom fishing method and is of particular importance in the harvesting of demersal or ground fish including cod, haddock and hake and flat-fish species such as plaice and flounder. The fish are surrounded by warps (rope) laid out on the seabed with a trawl shaped net at mid-length. As the warps are hauled in, the fish are herded into the path of the net and caught. Effectiveness is increased on a soft bottom by the sand or mud cloud resulting from the warps' movement across the bottom. This method of fishing is less fuel-intensive than trawling and produces a high quality catch, as the fish are not bumped along the bottom as with trawling.

Static gears

The effectiveness of static methods of fishing depends on the fish moving towards the gear which is set in a particular way and for a period of time in one place.

Gill nets are walls of netting which may be set at or below the surface, on the seabed, or at any depth in-between. Gill netting is probably the oldest form of net fishing having been in use for thousands of years. Depending upon how these nets are constructed and hung, they are referred to as either gill, tangle (more loosely constructed than gill nets) or trammel nets (formed of a loose sheet of netting between two large mesh sheets). Fish, which attempt to swim through the net, are caught if they are of a size large enough to allow the head to pass through the meshes but not the rest of the body. The fish then becomes entangled by the gills as it attempts to back out of the net. The mesh size used depends upon the species and size range being targeted.

Drift nets: Gill nets which are not set or fixed in any way, are in fact 'mobile', and allowed to drift with the prevailing currents. This type of gill net is called a drift net and is used on the high seas for the capture of a wide range of fish including, tuna, squid and shark and off north-east England for salmon.

Long-lines are one of the most fuel-efficient catching methods. This method is used to capture both demersal and pelagic fishes including swordfish and tuna. It involves setting out a length of line, possibly as much as 50-100 km long, to which short lengths of line, or snoods, carrying baited hooks are attached at intervals. The lines may be set vertically in the water column, or horizontally along the bottom. The species caught is determined by hook size and the type of bait used.

Other methods of line fishing include: trolling with lines whereby a boat is used to tow a number of baited lines through the water to attract fish; hand held or mechanically operated rods with baited hooks (pole and line) are used to catch fish which have been attracted to the surface by light or by chumming (the scattering of live or minced bait); the use of mechanised and hand held lines (handlines); and jigging. Jigging is widely used to capture squid. A jig is a type of grapnel, attached to a line, which may be manually or mechanically jerked in the water to snag the fish in its body. Jig fishing usually happens at night with the aid of light attraction.

Pots are small baited traps which can be set out and retrieved by the operating vessel. They are widely used on continental shelves in all parts of the world for the capture of many species of crustaceans and fish, together with octopus and shellfish such as whelks. Potting is a highly selective method of fishing and potentially sustainable. However, in Britain, fishing effort in the potting sector is high with currently no restrictions on the number and type of pot used or the amount of shellfish taken. Pots used to be constructed from 'withy' or willow, but are now constructed from plastic-coated or galvanised wire with nylon netting. This makes them virtually indestructible. Modern pots or 'parlour pots' are also more complex and fitted with 'pot-locks', making escape impossible for the crab or lobster entering it. These factors combined with mechanical hauling allow fishermen to haul more pots and to leave them on the seabed for longer thus increasing efficiency and fishing capacity.

Seine netter

Other methods include harpooning with hand-operated gear for the capture of large, high value species such as basking sharks; traps; and divers. In some countries such as the Philippines, explosives (dynamite fishing) are used on reefs to capture fish. This is a particularly destructive method of fishing and is

Grouper

prohibited within waters of the European Union and many other regions. Cyanide is also used by fishermen in many areas of South East Asia, the Pacific and the Indian Ocean to stun reef fish such as grouper and Napoleon wrasse which are then exported for the live reef fish food market.

Industrial fisheries

Most fishing methods target fish for direct human consumption. Fisheries targeting species for indirect human consumption or for reduction purposes i.e. the manufacture of fish oil and meal, are referred to as industrial fisheries. Fishmeal and oil is produced almost exclusively from small, pelagic species, for which there is little or no demand for direct human consumption. The method of capture is purse-seining and trawling with small mesh nets in the range of 16-32 mm. Important industrial fisheries in South America include the Chilean jack mackerel fishery and the Peruvian fishery for anchoveta. Industrial species in the North Sea and north-east Atlantic include sandeel, sprat, capelin, blue whiting, Norway pout and horse mackerel. Fish oil is used in a range of products including margerine and biscuits. Fishmeal and oil has more widespread use however in the manufacture of pelleted feedstuffs for intensively farmed poultry, pigs and, not least, aquaculture (see Chapter 5).

Sandeels

Chapter Five

Aquaculture

Introduction

Although farming of fish can be traced back to ancient times, most notably in China, the farming of trout as a commercial activity has only been developed in the 20th century. Similarly, salmon farming is a modern innovation, having commenced on a commercial scale only in the last two decades.

> *Aquaculture is the general term given to the cultivation of any aquatic (fresh and marine) species (plant or animal). When the cultivation takes place in marine or salt water the term mariculture is also applied.*

Production

Total world marine aquaculture production was estimated at 13.1 million tonnes in 1999. This represents 13.5% of total world marine fisheries production and 10.5% of all world fisheries production. Including inland or fresh-water fisheries, aquaculture represents 26% of total fisheries production.

> *Today approximately 1 in 5 fish destined for the dinner table world-wide is farmed*

Due to a growing world population and changes in eating habits, demand for fish is increasing. Current estimates indicate that by the year 2010 the world will need to increase its production of food fish by some 30 million tonnes (Mt) to which aquaculture will be a major contributor.

The major contribution from aquaculture will be from fresh water cultivation of herbivorous species such as tilapia and carp. It is also likely that more of the world's catch currently used for animal feed will be used for direct human consumption.

Two of the main attractions to suppliers of farming fish over capture fisheries or wild caught fish, are greater efficiency and a steadier supply of fish.

> *Aquaculture supplies 6-7% of the total weight of seafood to Europe*

Aquaculture produces four principal groups of commodities:

Fin fish - of which the largest volume by far is accounted for by non-carnivorous species, such as carp, tilapia and milkfish. In the carnivorous group salmonids, catfish and yellowtail dominate. Strict marine carnivores such as halibut, turbot, cod and bass, which is extensively farmed in southern Europe, are more demanding and require high quality proteins and oils.

Crustaceans - such as crayfish, crab, and lobsters (mainly for seeding populations) and penaeid shrimps (prawns) (in more tropical locations).

Molluscs - such as mussels, oysters, scallops and abalones.

Plants - such as seaweeds.

Aquaculture can be **extensive** - where husbandry is practised for only part of the organism's lifecycle, or **intensive** - where it is provided throughout the entire lifecycle.

In the simplest, extensive aquaculture, young fish are stocked in ponds or enclosures and harvested some time later having depended on natural foods.

Examples of extensive aquaculture include cultivation of the edible seaweed *Porphyra*, used for Nori production in Japan. The weed is grown in coastal waters on ropes suspended from rafts. Various seaweeds, or marine macroalgae are used as human food in many parts of the world, most notably in Japan. Animal species, such as oysters and mussels, are also cultivated extensively.

In many developed countries most or all of aquaculture is intensive. Fish are fed artificial diets in the form of pellets such as those used on prawn and salmonid farms.

Two examples of intensive aquaculture described here are intensive pond culture of panaeid shrimp (prawn) in Asia and cage culture of salmonids, which is widespread throughout many temperate waters.

Many aquaculture systems are monocultures i.e. species are separated throughout the growing-on period. However, in countries such as China and India, polyculture, in which several species are grown-on together is an important technique.

Shellfish farming

Oysters are bred in hatcheries and then grown on in the sea – usually in semi-rigid plastic mesh bags supported by steel trestles secured in intertidal waters. The species most commonly cultivated is the Pacific oyster *Crassostrea gigas*.

Mussels, such as the blue or common mussel, have a long history of use and cultivation in Britain and are one of the most important commercial species landed by weight. Although traditionally, natural mussel beds have been harvested, there is now more emphasis on farming mussels rather than exploiting wild stocks. They are induced to settle on ropes (hanging or floating culture) or suspended cages hung from rafts. This technique is extensively used in Spain and Scotland to cultivate the common mussel *Mytilis edulis*.

Mussels are filter feeders and require high quality water conditions for their cultivation. They are mainly herbivorous, eating phytoplankton, but also eat some zooplankton and organic detritus, which they filter from a current of water drawn by the gills into the shell cavity.

Scottish waters, particularly west-coast sea lochs, are well suited to mollusc production and numerous mussel farms produce small quantities by hanging culture.

Another method of cultivation is by bottom culture. In this method seed (juvenile) mussels are transplanted from natural beds to 'lays' in sheltered areas for growth. The Menai Straits' lays, in Wales, account for 50% of UK mussel production.

Extensive cultivation of mussels and oysters is a low-impact farming activity, provided it is carried out in an environmentally responsible manner. Both mussels and oysters are plankton feeders and obtain all their nutrition from the waters in which they live. Whilst spat or seed may be removed from wild stocks, or commercially produced in laboratories, mussel spat may also settle naturally on the ropes when they are hung out in the spring.

Impacts of mussel and oyster cultivation include increased competition for food with other wild filter-feeding animals; faecal waste production; and interaction with natural predators such as starfish and eider ducks, which must be excluded from the beds. Eiders can be humanely discouraged from taking too many mussels by the simple presence of workers around the mussel ropes during their main feeding times.

The Soil Association (see Chapter 2) is developing standards for organic mussel production in the near future.

Water Quality

Many shellfish are filter feeders and require clean water to ensure that their flesh does not become contaminated with pollutants. The quality of shellfish and shellfish waters are regulated by EC Directives. The Shellfish Hygiene Directive protects consumers by laying down bacteriological and chemical standards for live bivalves such as mussels and oysters. European countries are required to designate bivalve production areas and categorise them according to the treatment required before they can be sold for human consumption. Shellfish harvesting areas are classified according to levels, or counts of faecal bacteria present in the shellfish: 'Class A' is reserved for shellfish which comply with the requirements of the Directive without purification. Shellfish from 'Class B' areas are required to be held in clean sea water in purification tanks, or purified by heat treatment, before they can be placed on the market. 'Class C' is reserved for shellfish requiring relaying or heat treatment. The Directive prohibits the production of shellfish from non-categorised areas or where the limits for Class C are exceeded.

To buy mussels from consistently A Class waters, many large retailers import from France, Denmark and Holland. However, this lack of support for UK shellfish has more to do with the classification system in these countries rather than the quality of their shellfish waters. Currently 3% of shellfish waters in England and Wales and 85% in Scotland are classified as Class A. The Marine Conservation Society is working to address the disparity between the interpretation of the Directive in UK and in Europe.

Several and Regulating Orders

Shellfish species (scallops, mussels, clams and cockles) are often managed by what are referred to as Several and Regulating Orders.

A 'Several Order' gives an individual, company, or corporation the exclusive right to fish for named shellfish species within a given area.

A 'Regulating Order' is similar to a Several Order except it bestows upon the beneficiary the right to manage and regulate a fishery, or a number of fisheries within a large area.

The Shetland Shellfish Management Organisation (SSMO) (set up by a number of fishermen's organisations including the Shetland Fishermen's Association) has obtained a Regulating Order to manage all shellfisheries within 6 miles of Shetland's shoreline (600,000 hectares). Since 2000, SSMO has introduced a restrictive licensing scheme along with other measures to conserve fish stocks, including a lobster restocking programme and a maximum creel limit for fishing boats. The SSMO is hoping to obtain Marine Stewardship Council (MSC) certification (see Chapter 2) for some or all of the shellfish fisheries around Shetland, as are various oyster fisheries in England and Wales. The Burry Inlet cockle fishery in west Wales already has MSC certification.

Prawn farming

Salt and brackish-water pond culture is the prevalent system in many Asian and South American countries including Thailand, Malaysia, Indonesia, the Philippines, Ecuador, Mexico and Guatemala.

Prawns (*Panaeus spp.*) are widely cultivated for the export market. It is a valuable commodity accounting for 20% of the total value of internationally traded fishery products. The giant tiger prawn is the most commonly cultivated species in South-East Asia, and Thailand is currently the major prawn-culturing nation in the world. Major importers include the USA (50% of global production), Japan and Europe, of which Spain is the main importer of fresh and frozen prawn among the EC countries.

Prawn is reared in man-made ponds. This can cause problems for sustainability associated with; mangrove habitat destruction; depletion of fresh water supplies; and the processing of wild caught fish for feed pellets. In Thailand for example, the amount of fish processed into animal feed has increased by more than 25% in the last decade.

Although prawns have been cultivated in ponds in tropical regions for some time, it is only in the last 2-3 decades that the process has become an industrial or intensive one.

Impacts of prawn cultivation
There are a range of environmental and social impacts caused by prawn farming:

- Deforestation
- Coastal erosion
- Decline in local fisheries
- Removal of 'fry' or broodstock causing depletion of wild stocks
- Habitat destruction (including land subsidence due to water extraction)
- Pollution (from pesticides, chemicals and artificial feed)
- Disease (high-stocking densities of shrimp cause outbreaks of disease and the use of anti-biotics to control them)
- Displacement of indigenous people from traditional land
- Loss of traditional uses of habitat and resources e.g. charcoal, building materials, food, medicines etc.
- Loss of locally available protein and fresh water

Common Mussel

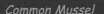

Deforestation

Mangrove forests are found throughout the coastal fringes of equatorial and tropical regions and are considered to be one of the most productive ecosystems in the world. They are under increasing threat, however, from coastal development, tourism, farming and prawn cultivation.

One of the major environmental impacts of prawn farming is clear felling of mangrove forests. In Ecuador, for example, damage to mangrove forests in some areas exceeds 90% of the total forested area.

> Over 50% of the world's mangrove forest has disappeared, over half of this due to prawn cultivation

Mangrove forests are important in that they provide stability to the coastline, preventing flooding, erosion and deposition of silt on near-by coral reefs. They also provide important habitat for birds such as cormorant and pelican, and are important nursery and spawning grounds for fish including prawns. Mangroves are also important 'sinks' for carbon dioxide, providing the basic functions of tropical rainforest.

Studies in Colombia have shown that 1 hectare of semi-intensively cultivated land (1 hectare produces about 4,000 kgs of prawn annually) for prawn production, requires between 38 and 198 hectares of natural ecosystem to supply the resources needed for the farm and to absorb and assimilate the wastes from it. Overall the environmental 'footprint' can be almost 200 times greater than that of the actual farm, with a concomitant reduction in real production to about 20 kg/hectare.

However, improvements have been made, in prawn cultivation in Asia since the boom in farming in the 1970s and 1980s, and there are now some well-run, efficient farms which provide employment for local people and generate income for impoverished economies.

Companies such as the Seafood Company, which comprises Anchor Seafoods, The Cromer Crab Company and Norfolk Shellfish, are actively involved in sourcing and promoting sustainably and ethically produced seafood, including farmed shrimp such as tiger prawns. The Company also subscribes to the Global Aquaculture Alliance (GAA) (see below) and is a member of the Ethical Trading Initiative (ETI) (see Chapter 9). Its farming policy incorporates many of the GAA standards as well as further enhancements in line with UK retail expectations. These cover such areas as mangrove protection, agriculture, conservation, and a requirement for farms to benefit local economies and community life.

Organic (see Chapter 2) prawn i.e. prawns grown without the use of pesticides or anti-biotics is now being produced in Vietnam and Ecuador. Lyons Seafood Ltd is currently the only company marketing organic prawns (white prawns) from Ecuador, which it supplies to the supermarket chain Sainsburys. No direct reference is made, however, on the packaging to mangrove protection.

The Global Aquaculture Alliance (GAA) is an international, non-profit trade association dedicated to advancing environmentally responsible aquaculture. Over several years it has been developing a Responsible Aquaculture Programme. The programme is designed to provide certified products to those who want assurance (see

Chapter 2) that it is environmentally responsible to buy farm-raised seafood. Although the initial programme focuses on prawns, many of its elements can be applied to other species.

Fish farming

Fishes that are successfully grown in cages include Atlantic salmon in Europe and America; Pacific salmon in America; the yellowtail in Japan; and seabass and groupers in Greece, Malaysia and Indonesia.

Scallop

In Britain, two species of fish are principally farmed: Atlantic salmon in salt-water and rainbow trout in fresh-water. This is changing with the introduction of new species such as cod, haddock and halibut.

Salmon farming

During the past decade, the global production of farmed salmon (chinook, Atlantic and coho) and large rainbow trout has grown from 378,000 tonnes in 1991 to 1.1 million tonnes in 2000.

Although Norway is still the largest producer of farmed salmon, Chile has increased its production faster than any other country and looks set to overtake Norway. The UK and Canada are the next producers after Norway and Chile. In 2000, the UK produced 124,000 tonnes of Atlantic salmon and 1,000 tonnes of rainbow trout, compared to 41,000 and 3,000 respectively in 1991. The most important market for salmon is Japan where it is popular as sashimi (raw fish) and the Japanese consume about 30% of the total supply.

Salmon farming is a huge, multi-national business, with the ownership of farms dominated by a few key players. The trend towards fewer but larger fish farming companies is likely to continue. Within five or six years it is possible that there will be just five or six companies controlling 90% of all salmon production. Very small producers serving niche markets (see below) are predicted to survive whilst medium-sized producers will be squeezed out. Examples of large salmon producing companies are Nutreco Holding and Pan Fish.

Nutreco, a Dutch conglomerate, owns just under half of salmon production in Scotland (where the majority of farmed salmon in the UK is produced), representing a global share of 20%. The remaining 50% is shared amongst approximately 75 companies. Relatively few independent Scottish companies remain, accounting for around 20,000 tonnes, or 20% of annual production in Scotland.

Examples of small independent Scottish companies are Loch Duart Ltd and Salar Ltd. Both are members of Scottish Quality Salmon (see Chapter 2).

Loch Duart Ltd owns some of the oldest farmed sites in Scotland. It produces 1,600 tonnes of Atlantic salmon each year, most of which is sold on the Continent. Rick Stein, TV chef and food writer, is quoted as saying that Loch Duart salmon 'is the closest to a wild salmon' he has ever seen or tasted from a farm. The quality of Loch Duart salmon is attributed to the priority given to the health and welfare of the fish and to the long-term protection of the environment. This has been achieved by a unique fallowing system, which allows each of the sea lochs to remain unused for one year in three. As in traditional rotation in land farming, one full year allows natural cleansing and regeneration. Stocking densities are also significantly lower than the average of 20-25 kg/m^3 and no antibiotics or anti-foulants have been used since 1994.

Salar Ltd of South Uist in the Outer Hebrides, also produces quality Atlantic salmon in addition to its award winning speciality product, Salar Flaky Smoked Salmon. Production currently stands at 500 tonnes a year and the whole operation - from freshwater hatchery to sea site, production and despatch – employs 17 members of staff. Although fish farming is often blamed for its adverse impact on the marine environment, a variety of wildlife is reported to flourish around the Salar farm. Species include otters, seals and seabirds as well as local fisheries for velvet crab and scallop.

Value to the Scottish economy

The salmon farming industry has been the single most important economic development in the Highlands and Islands of western Scotland for the past 30 years. It provides employment - approximately 6,500 people are employed in the salmon farming industry in Scotland - often in remote rural areas where alternative employment opportunities are limited. Unfortunately these areas also tend to be some of the most unspoiled and natural areas remaining, often conflicting with tourist and other interests. The ex-farm value of Scottish salmon produced is £300 million – greater than Highland beef and lamb together – with a retail value estimated at £600 million.

Life cycle of salmon and salmon production

Salmon are diadromous, that is they move during their life cycle between fresh and marine waters. The production of farmed salmon attempts to mirror this natural life cycle.

Broodstock fish are moved to fresh water to spawn. Spawning is generally carried out by artificial methods. Male and female fish are 'stripped' of their sperm and eggs and the eggs fertilised in a hatchery. Broodstock may be slaughtered prior to stripping. Fertilised eggs are kept in high quality fresh-water until they hatch. On hatching, the fry are kept in fresh water and fed pelleted food manufactured from fishmeal and fish oil (see below).

Fish are kept in tanks or fresh water cages until about 12 months old when they become smolts. At this stage the fish are transferred to seawater cages where the growth rate is higher. The fish reach market size after about two years at sea.

Cod

Marine cages are normally circular (between 50 and 100 m in circumference) or square (between 12 and 24 m^2) structures from which a net is hung to a depth of between 10 and 15 m. Cages are traditionally moored in sheltered areas such as sea lochs, although as cage and mooring design improves, siting cages in deeper and more exposed water is expected.

Prior to harvesting, fish are not fed for up to one week. This is nesessary for hygiene purposes to reduce the risk of bacterial contamination from the gut. At harvesting the fish are killed, bled, gutted and packed on ice for transport to fish processors. Slaughter of farmed fish in the UK is governed by an Act of Parliament. Fish were traditionally slaughtered by a method of percussive stunning with an instrument known as a 'priest' - a polypropylene baton weighing approximately 0.75 kg – followed by severing of the gill arches. Now an even quicker and more humane method is mechanical stunning which is widely used. Industry is also researching other methods such as electrical stunning. In organic production (see below) slaughtering by ice, carbon dioxide, suffocation (leaving fish to die in air) or exsanguination (bleeding) without stunning is prohibited. These methods are not commonly used in non-organic production as every effort is made to reduce stress during slaughter in order to maintain the quality of the flesh.

Impacts of fish farming

Salmon farming in Scotland is one of the most heavily regulated industries in Britain.

To develop a farm requires a lease from the Crown Estate Commission (CEC) – which owns the seabed below the low water mark - and consent from the Scottish Executive Environment Rural Affairs Department (SEERAD). This requires consultation with a list of key bodies and interested parties. Because of the dual role of the CEC as landowner and licensing authority, responsibility for authorisation has been transferred to the Local Authorities (LAs). An Environmental Impact Assessment (EIA) must also be carried out before a development consent can be considered.

The discharge of waste from fish farms in Scotland is controlled by the Control of Pollution Act (COPA) 1994. A 'consent to discharge' must be obtained from the Scottish Environmental Protection Agency (SEPA) for all discharges of effluent into controlled waters.

The main threats to aquatic systems come from emissions of products used during salmon production:

- Medicines e.g. antibiotics, and chemical therapeutants - are widely used to maintain the health of farmed stocks. However, due to extensive vaccination programs it is now extremely rare for antibiotics to be used. When they are used (legally) it is under veterinary guidance and the antibiotics are licensed.
- Sea lice treatments (a category of medicines) which may be applied as bath treatments e.g. hydrogen peroxide or as in-feed treatments e.g. SLICE (emamectin benzoate). The use of organophosphates is largely historical and is now markedly reduced with a ban introduced on the use of dichlorvos and the development of more efficacious and benign products such as hydrogen peroxide and SLICE.
- Micro-nutrients - such as zinc added to fish feeds may increase nutrient levels in sediments below cages.
- Nutrients, especially ammonia - are released to the environment via waste food and fish faeces.

Other concerns about fish farming are those associated with disease; dependence on wild harvested stocks for manufacture of fish-feed; the impact of farming on wild salmon stocks; and more recently the introduction of genetically modified (GM) or transgenic fish.

Disease

Infectious Salmon Anaemia (ISA) (which does not affect humans) is of particular concern, as one of the major problems with this disease is that the virus incubates for several months before expressing symptoms, which creates problems for managing the disease. The disease can lie dormant for up to 6 months until the fish are stressed by cold, other disease, or treatment for parasites.

Salmon farming has also been implicated in a recent epidemic of Amnesic Shellfish Poisoning (ASP) which broke out in the summer of 1999, along the west and north coasts of Scotland. ASP is caused by a build-up of toxic algae, on which shellfish, such as scallops, feed. Although no link has been proven between the disease and caged fish, some critics think that high levels of ammonia, associated with salmon production (7,000 tonnes per year produced by Scottish salmon farming), cause the toxic algae responsible for ASP, to proliferate.

Fish feed

Salmon are carnivorous and therefore the welfare and production of healthy stock demands that captive fish are fed appropriately.

The main producers of fishmeal are Chile and Peru, which account for about 50% of total production. Fishmeal and oil are derived from industrial fishing for small pelagic, notably clupeid (sprat and anchovy), species (see Chapter 4) and is the main component of fishmeal fed to farmed salmon in the UK. Production of fish oil was estimated at 1.2 million tonnes and fishmeal at 6.5 million tonnes in 2000.

Fish oils are needed in marine feeds to ensure adequate production of omega 3 fatty acids (see Chapter 7) in farmed fish. Alternative sources are plant proteins such as soya bean. Soya bean, although able to provide adequate protein, is deficient in certain amino acids essential for growth.

> It is estimated that as much as 5 kgs of wild fish is required to produce 1 kg of farmed fish

Apart from the inefficiency of feeding wild caught fish to farmed fish, the production of fishmeal relies heavily on harvesting huge quantities of fish at or near the base of the food-chain (see Chapter 8). However, only 12% of the fishmeal produced globally is fed to farmed fish, the remaining 88% is fed to factory-farmed omnivorous animals such as pigs and chickens.

As demand for fish for direct human consumption increases, it is predicted that the amount of fish available for reduction purposes (i.e. manufacture of fishmeal and oils) will decline. It is expected that supplies will be met from: the utilization of fish currently thrown away or discarded (see Chapter 8) due to changes in the law (currently about one third of the world's global catch is discarded annually as by-catch); increasing use of and research into alternative proteins; and the use of organic feed (see below).

Wild salmon stocks

Considerable concern has been voiced over the effect salmon farming may be having upon wild populations of salmon in Scotland. Half a million farmed fish are estimated to have escaped from Scottish farms in 2000 (this represents about 0.7% of the number of fish produced annually) and escapees are reported to outnumber wild caught fish by a factor of 7 to 1. Interbreeding of farmed fish with wild fish could alter their genetic

Diver checking mussel ropes

makeup and have an adverse impact on their capacity for survival. Escaped salmon can also transmit disease and parasites (sea lice) to wild fish. Recent studies indicate that sea lice infestation may have a considerable impact upon the survival of young salmonids (salmon and sea trout) migrating to sea. Good cage design and preventative maintenance can help reduce the number of fish escaping.

GMO Salmon

Genetically modified organisms (GMOs) are essentially transgenic organisms i.e. organisms that have had foreign genes inserted into their cells. The most widespread modification of fish species, including Atlantic salmon, is the insertion of growth genes, for increased growth and efficiency and anti-freeze protein (from Arctic species) for increased cold tolerance and growth.

To date, most of the research and development of GM fish has been carried out in Canada where 'super' salmon with growth rates up to 8 times faster than normal fish are being produced. However, these fish have lower survival rates and may not be commercially viable. Research is being carried out in UK laboratories, mainly on carp and tilapia species, although the techniques may soon be applied to salmon and cod.

Environmental concerns for GM fish focus mainly on their introduction to the natural marine environment from the accidental escape of genetically modified farmed fish. In Norway, for example, escapees make up about 30% of the salmon in rivers and outnumber the resident salmon in many inland streams. It is feared that because GM salmon are larger, more voracious and more aggressive, they will compete with and eventually displace wild native species. Companies developing GM technology argue that because transgenic salmon have a very low fitness they will be unable to compete successfully in the wild. However, any inter-breeding is likely to lead to genetic dilution and reduced fitness amongst wild fish.

Although no transgenic aquatic species are yet available to the consumer, transgenic fish may well be on the market within the next few years. The EU has stated that it will allow the import and sale of GM or transgenic salmon provided it meets European Community safety and environment standards. It will be up to UK producers, retailers and consumers to ensure GM fish do not become available in Britain.

Although no aquatic GMOs are currently being traded, GM soya bean is an ingredient of shrimp and other animal feeds that are traded globally. In Britain, however, there is an industry-wide initiative to source non-GMO salmon feed.

Salmon farm in Scottish sea loch

Reducing the impact of salmon farming
Improvements, many of them consumer-driven, are being made all the time to reduce the impact of salmon farming on the marine environment. For example, Marks & Spencer, which for many years has set standards for farmed salmon through its own Codes of Practice, launched a 'Salmon Select Farm' scheme in early 2001. The scheme builds on existing Codes but adds new requirements to demonstrate year on year reduction in environmental impact and use of medicines. Growers are ranked in order of compliance with Key Performance Indicators such as water quality (oxygen content, water flow etc.) and prevalence of sea lice for example. Selected farms are also required to draw up Veterinary Health Plans to improve fish health through good husbandry.

An example of an industry driven initiative to improve the environmental performance of the fish-farming industry is the Sustainable Development Strategy developed by Scottish Quality Salmon (SQS) (see Chapter 2). The strategy involves rigorous environmental assessment and includes an Environmental Management System (EMS) designed to help members extend their exsisting control measures in order to meet the requirements of the international standard ISO 14001. (EMSs are a systematic way of addressing environmental issues associated with an organisation's activities, products and services). In addition to participation in a Product Certification Scheme, all SQS members are required to sign up to this Strategy.

The future of fish farming
Industry predictions are that production of farmed Atlantic salmon will increase to approximately 160,000 tonnes by 2007. It is anticipated that 30,000 tonnes can be accommodated within exsisting farms, whilst another 50-100 sites will be needed to achieve the total. The most suitable sea lochs are perhaps already being farmed close to the limits of their carrying capacity. However as cage design and mooring technology improves, some operators are moving to 'open' sea sites, which results in a wider dispersal of effluent and thus fewer environmental effects.

Many environmental groups, most notably WWF and Friends of the Earth Scotland, are however calling for a moratorium on increasing salmon production. There is also widespread support for the current inquiry into the impact of the salmon farming industry on the marine environment and a call for reform in Scottish aquaculture.

New species

In the UK, it is widely predicted that over the next 10 years major changes will take place in the fish farming industry. There is likely to be a wider range of farmed species such as cod, halibut, haddock and Arctic charr, as well as warm water species, utilising waste heat from thermal discharges.

Atlantic cod has been a staple food fish for almost 1,000 years, but cod has been overfished and the sizes of landings are now controlled by quota. Development of new farming techniques and depletion of wild stocks are major factors contributing to the commercial potential of farming cod.

The first consignment of Norwegian farmed cod was bought by Tesco in 1998. In 1997, Marks & Spencer invested about £50,000 in a three-year project to farm 50 tonnes of cod in Scotland. (The annual market for cod in the UK is about 170,000 tonnes, more than 70% of which is imported from Iceland and Norway). The first consignment of 10 tonnes went on sale in 30 stores in 2000. Juveniles are transferred to on-growing tanks at an age of about six months for rearing on to market size. Target weight for marketing is a minimum of 2 kg, which is achieved after less than 24 months on-growing in salmon-type sea cages. New hatcheries are predicted to lead to the annual production of 5,000 tonnes of farmed cod by 2006.

Halibut farming is still a small industry in the UK, with current annual production at around 35 tonnes, although industry experts estimate that it could grow to 10,000 tonnes annually in the next decade. At present, one of the main limits to growth is the lack of sufficiently high quality eggs for on-growing. Unlike salmon, which produce fewer but much larger eggs, halibut produce as many as one million eggs, many of which are lost. At present there are only four halibut hatcheries in the UK.

The latest whitefish species to be farmed on an experimental basis in the UK is haddock. Over 50,000 tonnes of wild-caught haddock are consumed each year, most of which is imported.

Sustainable fish farming

Small-scale quality production

Fish farming can be sustainable and compatible with conservation needs provided farming is carried out in a responsible manner, on a small-scale, and the fisheries from which fish is derived for the manufacture of fish feed are managed properly. Industrial fishing for reduction purposes [explained earlier] is likely however to remain a major ecological and ethical issue for farming of carnivorous fish.

Small-scale producers realise the importance – both economic and environmental - of producing smaller amounts of quality salmon as opposed to mass-production, which is often achieved at the expense of the marine environment. Scottish Natural Heritage (SNH), the Government Statutory Agency with responsibility for nature conservation in Scotland, has recently endorsed the farming practice of Loch Duart Ltd as 'being operated in a sustainable and conservation friendly manner'.

Salmon in sea cages

Organic farmed fish

The Soil Association, (see Chapter 2) Food Certification Scotland and the Organic Food Federation have jointly developed aquaculture standards for organically farmed fish in the UK.

The basic characteristics of organic fish farming systems are:

- Sustainable use of the aquatic ecosystem (maintenance of water quality etc).
- Fish free from artificial ingredients.
- Health and welfare of fish.
- The prohibition of synthetic pesticides (the use of hydrogen peroxide is permitted).
- Use of local goods and services adhering to organic principles.

Organic fish feed

The minimum requirements for organic fish feed are:

- A minimum of 50% of the feed of aquatic origin must be derived from the by-products (e.g. whitefish trimmings and offal etc.) of wild caught fish for (direct) human consumption.
- The remaining 50% must be from fisheries certified as sustainable by an approved certification body (such as Marine Stewardship Council).
- Feed ingredients of agricultural origin (e.g. soya bean) must be from organically certified sources.
- Growth hormones etc. are prohibited (this is true of all salmon feed).
- Genetically modified organisms (GMOs) or products/ingredients derived from them are prohibited (true of all salmon feed).

The world's largest fish feed manufacturer is EWOS – the first feed manufacturer to gain Soil Association organic status.

Fish farming abroad

Fish farming is widespread throughout the Mediterranean and in terms of production is considered to be as successful as salmon farming. Fish farming is growing largely in response to the declining availability of fish from capture fisheries. For example, in

Italy farmed seafood now represents about 30% of its total seafood production. Other top producing countries include Greece, Spain, France and Portugal. The most prominent commercially farmed species are European sea bass and gilthead sea bream. Tuna is farmed in Italy and Spain mostly for the Japanese market. Tuna is caught at sea by specialized fishing units in the spring and summer, when their weight is approximately

Oyster platter

150 kg, then they are reared and fattened between July and December at farms until they reach about 180kg. Sturgeon is also farmed in the Mediterranean and in France, on the Biscay coast, for its meat and eggs or caviar.

Sea Ranching

Other ways of increasing the productivity of our seas and oceans include: transplanting young fish to

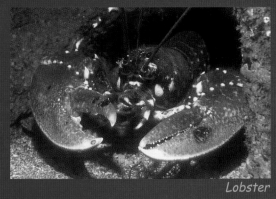

Lobster

areas of more abundant food; increasing the fertility of the seas; the construction of artificial reefs, which act as fish attracting or aggregating devices; and sea ranching.

Sea ranching provides one of the best possibilities for greatly increasing some fish and shellfish production. In the process, artificially reared juveniles of marine species are released directly to the open sea and later recaptured after growing to market size. The system may require modifications of the physical environment, such as the construction of artificial reefs, or protection from and enhancement of nursery and grow – out areas to improve the survival rate of released fish, and common property management in capture fisheries at the time of recapture.

Sea ranching has evolved most rapidly in Japan, partly as a result of the adoption of the 200 nm Exclusive Economic Zone (EEZ) regulation amongst coastal nations, thus limiting the fishing areas available to Japanese fishermen, and partly as a result of the oil crisis in the 1970s which discouraged fishing in the high seas. These changes forced Japan to maximise the use of its own coastal waters.

Sea ranching has not developed on a large scale in UK waters largely because of 'historic' fishing rights which allow several other nations to fish in our coastal waters within the 6-12 mile belt of the Territorial Sea. However, within the 6 mile limit juvenile lobsters reared in hatcheries have been released to boost wild populations. V-notching schemes have also been adopted on a regional basis in a bid to protect egg-bearing females and prevent further declines in stocks. V-notching is the removal of a small v-shaped piece of tail segment from the tail of an egg-bearing or 'berried' lobster that is then returned to the sea. The notch takes about 2 years to disappear. Byelaws introduced by Sea Fishery Committees (SFCs) make it an offence to be in possession of a V-notched lobster. Since 1997, the North Eastern Sea Fisheries Committee has been notching about 2,500 lobsters per year to achieve its initial target of 10,000 notched lobsters in four years. The only commercial lobster hatcheries in Britain are in Anglesey, Orkney and Padstow, Cornwall. The hatchery at Padstow has a visitor's centre where visitors discover how the hatchery is contributing to conservation and see live lobsters develop from an egg, still attached to a female, into a juvenile ready to be released into the wild.

Haddock

Chapter Six
Management of Fisheries

Introduction

Up until the Second World War (WWII) and the industrialisation of fisheries, the wealth of aquatic resources was assumed by many to be 'an unlimited gift of nature'. This myth has since faded in the face of realization, that although aquatic resources are renewable, without effective management they are not infinite. Fish stocks are a valuable resource and provide social and economic benefits and if properly managed, are capable of replenishing themselves indefinitely to provide a sustainable yield for man. Mismanagement leads in some cases, as in the Grand Banks cod fishery off Newfoundland, to stock collapse and indefinite closure of fishing grounds entailing economic losses and social disruption. The overall objective of fisheries management is, therefore, to ensure sustainable use of fish stocks.

Management in UK territorial waters

Management of commercial fish stocks and fisheries is the responsibility of a number of national Government departments, statutory agencies and local associations or committees.

Department for Environment, Food and Rural Affairs (DEFRA)

A new department for environment (formerly Department of the Environment, Transport and the Regions (DETR)), food (formerly Ministry of Agriculture, Fisheries and Food (MAFF)) and rural affairs was created in 2001. The new department brings together all the functions and responsibilities of the former DETR and MAFF. Crucial to DEFRA is its responsibility towards sustainable use of natural resources, which includes fisheries and protection of wildlife and habitat, both marine and terrestrial. The Food Standards Agency (FSA) now has responsibility for quality, nutrition and food safety aspects of consuming fish.

The Scottish Executive Environment and Rural Affairs Department (SEERAD), National Assembly for Wales Agricultural Department (NAWAD) and Department of Agriculture and Rural Development (DARD) have similar responsibilities for the management of marine and fishery resources in Scotland, Wales and Northern Ireland respectively.

Sea Fisheries Committees

In England and Wales, Sea Fisheries Committees (SFCs) have a statutory role in the regulation of inshore or coastal waters out to the 6 nautical mile (nm) limit. SFCs are empowered to make byelaws and can impose regulations on all fishing vessels within their jurisdiction for the management and conservation of fisheries. Examples of byelaws include setting minimum landing sizes (MLS) for fish (these have to be equal to or greater than those imposed by national or European legislation) and prohibitions on collecting certain fish and shellfish species and gear types for example. Many SFCs manage 'V-notching schemes for lobster (see Chapter 5). There are 12 SFCs funded by local authorities with appointees representing County Councils, fishermen and other local interests. SFCs also have responsibilities for the environment and marine conservation subsequent to recent changes in the law. In England and Wales, the Environment Agency has responsibility for management of migratory salmon fisheries out to 6 nm and acts as the SFC in some parts of the coast. In Scotland, inshore fisheries are regulated under the Inshore Fishing (Scotland) Act 1984 and administered by the Scottish Executive. Similar arrangements apply in Northern Ireland.

Producer and Fishermen's Organisations

Producer organisations (POs) were originally established by the European Commission to assist groups of fishermen to market their catches. Nowadays they also have responsibilities for managing their share or quota of the total allowable catch (TAC) agreed for stocks subject to restrictions under the Common Fisheries Policy (see below). There are approximately 20 POs in the UK. The Scottish Fishermen's Organisation is perhaps the largest PO representing around 60% of fishermen in Scotland.

Two significant Fishermen's Organisations are the National Federation of Fishermen's Organisations (NFFO) and the Scottish Fishermen's Federation (SFF). These organisations represent fishermen at the political level.

European framework

What is the Common Fisheries Policy?

Within European Union (EU) waters management of fisheries is regulated by the Common Fisheries Policy (CFP) and by national policy and legislation within the adjacent Faroese, Icelandic and Norwegian waters.

The CFP was created to manage a common resource (fish stocks) and to meet the objectives of the Treaty of Rome, the Treaty that established the European Community in 1957. The CFP has four main components: a marketing policy; an external policy; a structural policy; and a conservation and enforcement policy. The principles of the CFP were formally established in 1983 with the adoption of the latter policy. Fishing interests in European waters are currently represented by 15 Member States. This number is likely to increase as the European Union is enlarged in the coming years.

The CFP seeks 'to harmonise biological, economic and social objectives in a single management policy'. Economic and political priorities combined with the CFPs policy of equal access for all Member States to each other's fishing zones has undoubtedly contributed to the overexploitation of fish stocks and the erosion of marine resources. To date, the CFP has failed to deliver sustainable exploitation of fisheries resources with many stocks at present being outside safe biological limits.

Total allowable catches (TACs) and quotas

One of the objectives of the Conservation Policy is the sharing, or allocation of resources to Member States. The 'cornerstone' of this is the regulation of fisheries by the fixing of a system of Total Allowable Catches (TACs) and Quotas.

Total Allowable Catches (TACs) are agreed annually for each protected species in waters administered by the CFP. TACs are then divided nationally, with each Member State receiving a specified percentage or quota of the TAC. Quotas are allocated to Member States on the basis of 'relative stability'. The principle of relative stability is one of the fundamental principles

Monkfish

underlying the CFP. It guarantees a fixed percentage of the TAC for each species, irrespective of variation in the TAC, and is applied to allocate to the Member States a quota of the TAC for a given stock for which they have access. This quota is based on historic catches and the provision of Hague Preferences - these refer to special provisions for areas heavily dependent upon fishing declared at a Council meeting in The Hague in 1976. Examples of areas considered heavily dependent on fishing include parts of Scotland and Ireland. Another criterion for allocation is the loss of catches suffered by some Member States as a result of third countries extending their fishing limits to 200 nm. For example, British fishing boats lost access to distant water fisheries in Icelandic waters when Iceland extended its fishing limits. The quotas derived from these criteria and agreed in 1982 are regarded as 'Key' allocations and provide the basis for adopting quotas in subsequent years.

Each Member State has responsibility for dividing and monitoring the uptake of the quotas allocated. When a TAC is exhausted the fishery is closed. Member States are obliged to keep the European Commission regularly informed of their quota uptake to allow the situation to be monitored at Community level.

Scientific advice
Stock levels are assessed annually, and at the end of each year, TACs are fixed at a Fisheries Meeting of Council Ministers in December. The TACs are derived from proposals put forward by the European Commission and are based on scientific advice provided by the International Council for the Exploration of the Sea (ICES) - the international forum for fishery research and management (see Figure 1). This advice is subject to variation by that given by the Commission's Scientific, Technical and Economic Fisheries Committee (STEFC).

Figure 1: ICES fishing areas

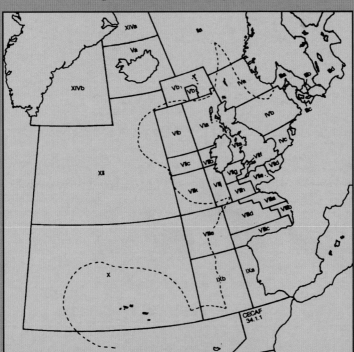

Stocks are described as being above (or inside) or below (or outside) Safe Biological Limits. When stock levels are described as outside biological limits they are so low that the ability of the stock to reproduce itself becomes seriously or increasingly impaired or threatened. Many stocks in European waters including the North Sea are considered to be outside these safe biological limits (see Table 1).

Table 1: Assessment of main fish stocks by ICES Areas
(Source: ICES ACFM 2001)

Species	North Sea IV	West of Scotland VIa & VIb	Irish Sea VIIa	E & W Channel VII (d&e)	Celtic Sea VII (f&g)	Western Stocks
Cod	O	O & NK	O	O & O	-	-
Haddock	H	H	H	-	NK	-
Herring	O	O & -	NK	-	NK	-
Mackerel	O	-	-	-	-	H
Plaice	O	-	W	H & O	-	-
Saithe	W	W & -	-	-	-	-
Sole	H	-	W	W & O	O	-
Sprat	NK	-	-	NK	-	-
Whiting	O	O & NK	O	O & W	-	-
Hake	-	-	-	-	-	O
Megrim	-	NK	-	-	-	H
Monkfish	-	H	-	-	-	O

O = Stock is outside safe biological limits
W = Stock is within safe biological limits
H = Stock is being harvested outside safe biological limits i.e. fishing level is too high
NK = No information
- = Species is not assessed in the area

TACs have a twofold purpose: they serve as the basis for dividing catch rights between Member States, and also to control fishing mortality rates. Although the CFP provides for a number of measures to control fishing effort and conserve stocks, such as the introduction of areas in which fishing is prohibited and economic incentives to encourage more selective fishing, the main instrument for controlling fishing is the system of TACs and quotas. This system of managing resources, particularly of mixed demersal or whitefish stocks, has been heavily criticised because of associated problems of discarding or throwing away of non-target or over-quota fish (see Chapter 8).

In December 2000, a 50% cut in the annual quota for cod for 2001 was agreed as a preliminary measure for the recovery of cod stocks in the North Sea. The fact that

UK boats were unable to catch their quota for that, or the previous five years, suggests that the cod was not there to catch in the first place!

Despite fishing levels being too high or stocks being already outside safe biological limits, North Sea quotas for haddock and whiting were increased by 54% and 38% respectively for 2002! The

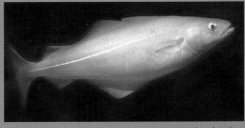
Saithe/Coley

quota for North Sea saithe (coley) was increased by 55%. Although this stock is considered to be above safe biological limits, saithe forms part of a complex, mixed fishery, with cod, haddock and whiting, and will inevitably result in discarding of over-quota or undersized cod, a species already on the brink of collapse.

Conservation measures

Conservation measures, which may be technical or non-technical, is the term given to legislative methods within the framework of the CFP which regulate the character of fishing activity. Technical measures such as minimum mesh and minimum landing sizes (MLS) and non-technical measures, such as closed nursery areas and seasonal closures, are designed to reduce mortality due to fishing, especially on small juvenile fish. This is to maintain stock sizes at levels higher than they would be in the absence of any regulation. In mixed demersal fisheries however, minimum mesh and landing sizes are a compromise and generally discriminate against larger species such as cod and saithe (coley).

For example, the minimum legal landing size for cod of 35 cm is not determined by biological factors. It merely represents the length at which 50% of fish entering a net of given mesh size (100 mm) are retained. Given the fact that cod in the North Sea is now smaller and fish mature at lower ages and smaller lengths, it is unlikely that substantial increases in mesh size will be implemented as a future measure to conserve stocks. However, the recently agreed Recovery Plan (EC 2056/2001) for cod in the

North Sea aims to encourage the use of bigger mesh sizes i.e. equal to or greater than 120 mm, by allowing all species caught above the legal minimum size restriction to be landed. Fishermen using mesh sizes smaller than 120 mm will be subject to restrictions on the amount of cod and other species retained on board and landed. Table 2 illustrates the discrepancy between current MLS for some species and their size at maturity.

Fishing on the high seas

Table 2: Minimum Landing Sizes (MLS) for selected UK species
(Source: MAFF 1999)

Species	Present Minimum Landing Size (MLS) (cm)	Size at which 50% of females first spawn (cm)	Maximum size attained by species (cm)
Cod	35	60 to 70	120 (average)
Haddock	30	30	76
Plaice	22	30 to 34	50 – 90
Whiting	27	20 to 22	70
Lemon sole	No MLS set	22	66
Sole	24	26 to 28	60 -70
Hake	27	50 +	60 – 100
Coley (Saithe)	35	52	130

In 1987 the Advisory Committee on Fishery Management (ACFM) showed that a minimum mesh size of 100 mm retains almost all (97%) 2 year old cod.
(Source: Holden 1994)

International framework

Regional Fisheries Organisations
In response to the global expansion of fisheries, international commissions, now referred to as Regional Fisheries Organisations (RFOs) (Table 3), emerged in the post war period (1950s) with responsibility for managing stocks in the high seas. Exploitation of fisheries on an international basis dominated until the late 1970s. Then, with the widespread introduction in the mid-seventies of exclusive economic zones (EEZs) and the adoption in 1982 of the United Nations Convention on the Law of the Sea (UNCLOS III), historic fishing patterns changed. The new legal regime of the ocean gave the coastal states rights and responsibilities for the management and use of fishery resources within their EEZs, creating the requirement for fisheries management frameworks to be adopted at national levels. Now 95% of what was formerly recognised as international waters or high seas, is under the jurisdiction of individual states.

The Food and Agriculture Organisation of the United Nations (FAO) was founded in 1945. It has 183 member countries and one member organisation, the European Community. Today, FAO is one of the largest specialised agencies in the UN and the lead agency for agriculture, forestry, fisheries and rural development. FAO's major programme on fisheries aims to promote sustainable development of responsible fisheries, with priority given to the implementation of its Code of Conduct for Responsible Fisheries (see below), and contribute to food security.

The International Council for the Exploration of the Sea (ICES) is an intergovernmental organisation supported by 19 Member Countries around the border of the North Atlantic. Established by international convention in 1902, ICES is the oldest intergovernmental marine science organisation in the world. Its role is to promote, co-ordinate and disseminate the results of research activities associated with the sea and its living resources. ICES provides advice on fish stocks and fisheries to three international fisheries commissions (the North East Atlantic Fisheries Commission (NEAFC), the International Baltic Sea Fishery Commission (IBSFC) and the North Atlantic Salmon Conservation Organisation (NASCO) (see Table 3). It also provides advice to the Governments of Member Countries, the European Commission and the Faroes and Greenland.

Table 3: Examples of Regional Fisheries Organisations (RFOs)

Acronym	Name	Area and species of responsibility
IBSFC www.ibsfc.org	International Baltic Sea Fisheries Commission	Baltic sea - All
CCAMLR www.ccamlr.org	Commission for the Conservation of Antarctic Marine Living Resources	Antarctic - All
CCSBT www.home.aone.net.au/ccsbt	Commission for the Conservation of Southern Bluefin Tuna	South Pacific - Bluefin tuna
IATTC www.iatc.org	Inter-American Tropical Tuna Commission	Eastern Pacific - Tuna & species taken in tuna fisheries e.g. marlin, swordfish etc.
ICCAT www.iccat.es	International Commission for the Conservation of Atlantic Tuna	Atlantic & adjacent seas - tuna & tuna-like species
IPHC www.iphc.washington.edu	International Pacific Halibut Commission	Pacific - Halibut
IWC www.iwcoffice.org	International Whaling Commission	Worldwide - Large whales (excludes small species e.g. pilot whales)
NAFO www.nafo.org	Northwest Atlantic Fisheries Commission	NW Atlantic – All commercial stocks
NASCO www.nasco.org.uk	North Atlantic Salmon Conservation Organisation	North Atlantic - Atlantic Salmon
NEAFC www.neafc.org	North East Atlantic Fisheries Commission	NE Atlantic – All including deep-water species which are currently an unregulated or unprotected resource under the NEAFC Convention

International agreements

United Nations Convention on the Law of the Sea (UNCLOS III)

Under UNCLOS III the freedom to fish by any one state must be exercised 'with due regard for the interests of other states in their exercise of the freedom of the high seas'. Accordingly, nations exploiting the same resources and fishing grounds are required to 'co-operate with each other in the conservation and management of living resources in areas of the high seas', through negotiation and by establishing Regional Fisheries Management Organisations (RFMOs) or RFOs.

FAO Code of Conduct for Responsible Fishing

The Code of Conduct for Responsible Fishing originated at the International Conference on Responsible Fishing held in May 1992 in Cancun, Mexico. The Code sets out principles and international standards of fishing practices with a view to ensuring the effective conservation, management, trade and development of living aquatic resources. It emphasises that the right to fish carries with it an obligation of responsibility.

The Code also adopts an ecosystem approach (Article 6.2) – the ecosystem approach to fisheries management promotes the importance of management measures that not only ensure the conservation of the target species, but also the ecosystem or species and habitat it interacts with - and endorses the precautionary approach (Article 6.5). The precautionary approach involves the application of prudent foresight. Taking account of the uncertainties in fisheries systems and the need to take (conservation) action even in the absence of complete scientific knowledge.

Whilst the Code is voluntary, certain parts of it are based on relevant rules of international law including those reflected in UNCLOS.

For example, an integral part of it is the 1993 FAO Agreement to Promote Compliance with International Conservation and Management Measures by Fishing Vessels on the High Seas (FAO Fishing Vessels Agreement) which has legal status, although it is not yet in force as only half the necessary countries have ratified the Agreement. This Agreement specifies the responsibilities of flag states over their fishing vessels and compliance with fishing rules.

UN Agreement on Straddling and Highly Migratory Stocks (UN Fish Stocks Agreement)

In the decade following the adoption of UNCLOS III fishing on the high seas became a major international problem. By the late 1980s it became clear that fisheries resources could no longer sustain the rapid and often uncontrolled rates of exploitation that had developed following the adoption of the Convention, which gave all states the freedom to fish without regulation on the high seas. Efforts to conserve and revitalise fish stocks within EEZs were being undermined by unregulated fishing activity on the high seas. Of particular concern was the unregulated exploitation of straddling and highly migratory species, which occur within and outside EEZs.

Examples of straddling stocks are pollack in the Bering Sea and cod which straddles international and Canadian waters. Examples of highly migratory species are tuna and swordfish. The Agreement introduces a number of measures, particularly in the area of environmental and resource protection, obliging states to adopt a precautionary approach to fisheries exploitation. This principle or approach to fisheries management

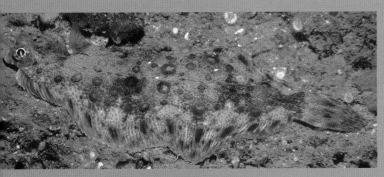
Lemon Sole

is enshrined in Principle 15 of the Rio Declaration 1992 on sustainable development. The UN Fish Stocks Agreement was one of the agreements to come out of the Earth Summit Convention on Biodiversity. The Agreement entered into force in December 2001.

UN Convention on Biodiversity

Widespread concern about the sustainability of present uses of natural renewable resources such as fisheries led to the United Nations Conference on the Environment and Development (UNCED), held in Rio de Janeiro, Brazil in 1992, also called the Earth Summit, and to the adoption of its Agenda 21.

Agenda 21 is the consensus document from the Earth Summit on how sustainable development should be implemented. Chapter 17 is of particular interest to fisheries managers and proposes several programmes including marine environmental protection and sustainable use and conservation of marine living resources.

Biodiversity Action Plans (BAPs)

The UK Government's response to the Biodiversity Convention, *Biodiversity: the UK Action Plan (UK BAP)*, published in 1994, sets out the broad strategy for conserving and enhancing wild species and wildlife habitats in the UK. A number of marine species, including a plan for commercial fish (cod, haddock, whiting, plaice, sole, herring, hake and mackerel), common skate, basking shark and deep-water fish, have been included in the UK BAP. A UK Biodiversity Steering Group, co-ordinated by DEFRA, will have responsibility for implementing the individual plans, which are voluntary.

The future for fisheries management

Review of CFP in 2002

In June 2001 the European Commission met in Brussels to launch a public hearing and debate on the future of the CFP. The focus of the debate was its 'Green Paper'. Published in March 2001, the Green Paper marks an important stage in the Review process of the CFP due to be completed in 2002. The Paper highlights the fact that the CFP has not delivered sustainable exploitation of fish stocks and will need to be changed if it is to do so. Importantly it identifies objectives for the future management of fisheries that include the health of the marine ecosystem as a basis for establishing responsible and sustainable fisheries.

Prawn

Future management and stakeholder interest

The need for better governance – the way in which decisions are taken – is widely acknowledged. The FAO describes fish stocks as belonging to, and part of, 'humanity's natural heritage' and as such suggests that their management should be 'a shared responsibility'. Historically, fish stocks have been managed for the exclusive and economic interests

Seabass

of commercial fishermen. This attitude is gradually changing as the wider interests of other groups (including conservation and angling interests) or 'stakeholders' are acknowledged.

As consumers, we are all stakeholders and can contribute to the responsible management of fish stocks by demanding that the fish we eat is from sustainably managed stocks and that the way in which it is caught causes minimum damage to the marine environment.

No Take Zones – an alternative fisheries management approach

The Marine Conservation Society (MCS) has campaigned for sustainable and sensitive fisheries since its formation in 1983. Currently, MCS is seeking the introduction of financial incentives for fishermen to switch to more environmentally and labour intensive methods of fishing and for the introduction of No Take Zones (NTZs) for managing fisheries. Both these initiatives are provided for in the current CFP, but are amongst the many management tools ignored by fisheries managers in favour of TACs and quotas.

NTZs are areas in which fishing and other extraction activities such as marine aggregate and oil production is prohibited. Currently only about 0.25% of the world's oceans are protected. In the USA, leading scientists are calling for 20% of the world's

oceans to be set aside as permanent biological reserves. In New Zealand they are aiming to achieve a target of protecting 10% of New Zealand's marine environment by 2010. New Zealand currently has 16 NTZs covering 762,841 hectares and representing 5% of the territorial sea out to 12 nautical miles.

The main advantage of NTZs over other fishery management tools is that they are designed to protect the marine ecosystem rather than single species. In northern European waters however there are currently no NTZs or areas in which fishing is permanently excluded for conservation or fish stock enhancement purposes, although there are areas within which fishing is prohibited for other reasons e.g. exclusion areas around oil rigs.

Young sea angler

Chapter Seven
Health & Welfare Issues

Human nutrition

Fish is an excellent source of nutrients and has an important role to play in our diet. It is a reliable source of protein, minerals (iron, selenium and iodine), vitamins and essential fatty acids. The livers of lean white fish are a particularly good source of vitamins A and D. The flesh of oil-rich fish, such as herring and mackerel, is an important source of the long chain omega 3 polyunsaturated fatty acids (PUFA). Fat or oily fish have a much higher nutritional value than white fish.

Protein

Fish is high in protein, essential for body-building and tissue repair. Most vertebrate fish contain 15-20 % protein, a little less on average than that contained in beef, pork or poultry meat, but more than in milk. Fish protein differs from that of meat in having less connective tissue and no elastin. The absence of tough elastin and the conversion of collagen into gelatin during cooking makes the protein of cooked fish easily digestible.

Vitamins

All fish are a good source of B vitamins, which are essential for the conversion of food to energy in the cells and for healthy nerve tissue. Oil-rich fish are the best natural source of vitamin D and a better source of the fat-soluble vitamins A and D than white fish or red meat. The livers of oily fish and lean white fish, however, contain even higher levels of vitamin A,D and E. Tuna and halibut liver oils have been reported to contain vitamin A levels as high as 10mg/100g and vitamin D levels as high as 50mg per 100g.

Minerals

Fish is a good source of calcium and phosphorous, needed for the formation of bones and teeth. Fish such as sardines, whose smallest bones are eaten, provide a rich source of these minerals. Fish is also a good source of iodine and fluorine, which are needed for the body's growth and metabolism. Fish is one of the few reliable sources of iodine, containing about 1 mg of iodine per kg compared with meat which contains about 0.05 mg per kg. Consequently, goitre – a disease caused by iodine deficiency – is rare in fish-eating populations. Oil-rich fish in particular is also a reliable source of selenium, an anti-oxidant associated with anti-ageing properties. Although fish are not generally a rich source of iron, sardines are an exception.

Fats and fatty acids

Fats (or lipids), composed of fatty acids, provide more than twice as much energy as carbohydrates or protein. Fatty acids comprise a string or chain of carbon atoms, to which are joined hydrogen atoms. Fatty acids can be saturated, monosaturated or polyunsaturated (PUFA) according to the structure of the carbon and hydrogen atoms.

The fatty acids in fish oils are much less saturated than the fatty acids of land animals, or the fatty acids in most vegetable oils. The fat found in all fish is mainly of the unsaturated type, which unlike saturated fats can reduce levels of cholesterol (see below) and lower blood pressure.

Fish store fat either in the flesh (oil-rich fish such as herring and mackerel) or in the liver (cod). The fat composition of fish, especially oily fish, is determined by a number of factors such as the time of the year and the type of feed available. They are generally fattest in late summer and early autumn and leanest after spawning in early spring. Over the period of a year the fat content of fish, such as herring and mackerel, can change from as little as 1% to over 30% by weight. Processing and cooking methods may also affect their nutritional composition.

Omega 3
There are two families of PUFA: the n-6 (or omega-6) family derived from the essential fatty acid, linoleic acid, and the n-3 (or omega-3) family which is derived from the essential fatty acid, alpha-linoleic acid. These two fatty acids are 'essential' i.e. they cannot be made in the body and have to be provided for in the diet.

Very long chain (i.e. with more than 18 carbon atoms) n-3 fatty acids (known as DHA and EPA) are found in abundance in fish oils and they are present in the flesh of oil-rich pelagic fish such as mackerel, salmon, herring, sprat, trout, sardine and pilchard. Tinned tuna is not a good source however due to a pre-cooking process which drastically reduces its EPA and DHA content.

Other sources of long chain n-3 fatty acids are meat (pork, beef and chicken) and butter (see Table 1) - all of which are saturated fats and not good for health.

n-3 fatty acids can also be synthesised in the body from alpha-linoleic acid found in plant-derived foods and ingredients, such as seed oils, some nuts and vegetables (see Table 2). These foods do not however contain long chain n-3 fatty acids.

Table 1: Sources of long chain n-3 fatty acids

Food	Average UK portion (g)	Total very long chain n-3 (per portion)	Total very long chain n-3 (per 100 g)
Roast beef	90	0.04	0.04
Chicken	100	0.06	0.06
Butter	10	0.01	0.1
Haddock	120	0.19	0.16
Tuna (in brine)	45	0.08	0.18
Cod	120	0.30	0.25
Plaice	130	0.39	0.3
Trout	230	2.65	1.15
Herring	119	1.56	1.31
Mackerel	160	3.09	1.93
Salmon	100	2.2	2.2
Kippers	130	3.37	2.59

Table 2: Sources of alpha-linolenic acid (omega-3)

Food	Content (g/100 g)
Cod and haddock	Trace
Roast beef, lean and fat	0.07
Chicken, light meat, roasted	0.07
Mackerel	0.22
Spinach. boiled	0.25
Mushrooms	0.27
Streaky bacon, grilled	0.27
Butter	0.46
Cod liver oil	1.10
Soya margerine	3.51
Rapeseed oil	9.60
Walnut oil	11.50

It has been recommended that an average 0.5% of total dietary energy should be obtained from EPA, DHA and other long chain n-3 PUFA (about 10g of long chain n-3 for men per week and 8g for women per week). The best way of increasing the amount of long chain n-3 PUFA and avoiding saturated fats is to eat more oil-rich fish.

Individuals should aim to eat an average of two portions per week of fish such as mackerel, herring, salmon, pilchard and sardine. Other sources are cod liver oil (1 x 5ml teaspoon per day) and fish oil concentrate capsules (4-5 1g capsules per day). Ask your pharmacist or doctor for advice.

Cholesterol
Cholesterol is a type of fat which is naturally produced by our bodies and is also found in the diet. It is essential for life, although too much of it circulating in the bloodstream is a problem, as it needs to be deposited. Deposition on the lining of the blood vessels causes hardening of the arteries and blood clots. Despite widespread health promotion campaigns, average levels have remained remarkably constant and are higher in the UK than in many other parts of the world. Because the type of fat found in oily fish is of the polyunsaturated variety small amounts can actually help to lower cholesterol levels. The nutritional value of fish with respect to protein, fat and cholesterol is summarised in Table 3.

Table 3: Nutritional value of raw fish (100g/4oz)
(Source: Jackson et al 2001)

Species	Energy kJ/kcal	Protein grams (g)	Total fats grams (g)	Cholesterol milligrams (mg)
Oysters	217/51	10.8	1.39	-
Haddock	308/73	16.8	0.6	36
Herring	970/234	16.8	18.5	70
Lemon sole	343/81	17.1	1.4	60
Cod	322/76	17.4	0.7	46
Halibut	390/92	17.7	2.4	50
Plaice	386/91	17.9	2.2	42
Salmon	757/182	18.4	12.0	50
Mackerel	926/223	19.0	16.3	55
Crab(cooked)	534/127	20.1	5.2	72

Health benefits of eating fish

The benefits of eating fish, especially oily fish, include: reduced chance of developing heart disease, increased longevity and lowering of blood pressure. Eating fish also ensures the proper development of the brain, nervous tissue and eyes of the foetus during pregnancy. It can also improve kidney function in severe diabetes and may improve inflammatory conditions such as arthritis and psoriasis.

Coronary heart disease
Coronary heart disease (CHD) is a major cause of death, particularly in the western world, but increasingly so elsewhere. Although CHD is predominantly a disease of old age, it is also responsible for many premature deaths (deaths occurring before age 65), particularly amongst men. Death rates from CHD in the UK (26% in 1991) are among the highest in the world.

CHD is a 'multifactorial' disorder. Factors causing CHD, some of which are controllable, include family history (i.e. it can be inherited), race, sex, age, smoking, exercise, stress and diet. Diet is an important and 'controllable' factor and can be modified by all. Dietary advice for the general population is to eat more fruit and vegetables, including pulses, peas and beans; more starchy foods such as potatoes, rice, pasta and bread; and more oil-rich fish.

There is some evidence to suggest that eating oil-rich fish, which is more or less a unique source of long-chain n-3 PUFA (EPA and DHA), can prevent heart disease.

Cancer

Cancer is the second most common cause of death in the UK. Although evidence is scarce for a beneficial role for fish oils in the prevention of human cancer, low incidence of breast cancer amongst Inuit and Japanese women whose diet is traditionally rich in fish, is notable.

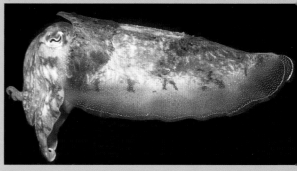

Cuttlefish

Immune disorders

Increased consumption of fish oils has been shown to suppress immune reactions and cause reduced inflammation in the treatment of immune disorders such as rheumatoid arthritis, multiple sclerosis and asthma. Although fish oils have been shown to alleviate some of the symptoms, the most valuable effects could be to enable sufferers to reduce their dependency on pain-relieving drugs, which sometimes have life-threatening side effects.

Eczema and skin disorders

Fish oils, particularly when combined with recognised drug therapies, can alleviate some of the symptoms associated with skin disorders such as psoriasis and eczema. Fish oils can significantly reduce itching, erythrema (reddening of the skin) and scaling.

Fish as 'brain food'

The long-chain n-3 fatty acid, DHA, found in oil-rich fish is essential for the development of the foetal brain and the retina. Inuit women, whose diet is rich in these fatty acids, produce characteristically high levels of DHA in their breast milk. Children who have been breast-fed and thus receive DHA in their mother's milk have been shown to perform better and have higher IQ levels than children who were bottle fed on formulae milk.

Fish welfare

Fish are sentient creatures and there is physiological evidence to support the fact that they feel pain and can also suffer from fear and distress. However, there are no guidelines governing the slaughter and processing of wild caught fish at sea. The slaughter of farmed fish on the other hand is more advanced and humane than virtually any other commercially exploited species (see Chapter 5).

Without doubt, fish are frequently gutted and sometimes frozen alive. When fish are taken in a net or on a hook they may suffer decompression as they rise towards the surface. As a result, the swim bladder (the gas filled organ controlling buoyancy) – not all fish have them – expands, often causing the gut to be pushed out through the mouth. Fish may also be crushed to death in the net or left to die from suffocation in air when landed on the deck.

Fair-fish, an organisation based in Switzerland, has defined criteria for humane methods of fishing and fish farming including criteria for the humane despatch of wild caught fish. Fish must be killed immediately after withdrawal from the sea by impact to the head. The sale of living fish is prohibited. More information available (translated from German) at www.fair-fish.ch

Oiled shellfish

Pollution in our seas and in our fish

In addition to pressures exerted on fish stocks by the fishing industry itself, there are many other human activities associated with exploitation of marine and land-based resources that can affect fish stocks and the seas they inhabit.

The main categories of pollution that affect the marine environment are nutrients, sewage, oil, hazardous and radioactive substances, heavy metals, litter (see ghost fishing Chapter 8), thermal discharges and noise and acoustic disturbance. Most of these have the potential to affect fishery resources and thus the fish we eat.

Effects of pollution on fishing and fish

Whilst nutrients are essential for life in the sea and their supply is the principal factor controlling primary production in the marine environment, excessive inputs as a result of human activities associated with agriculture and industry, cause nutrient enrichment or eutrophication in coastal waters to expand.

Eutrophication can cause both temporary and long term effects in marine ecosystems. Enhanced plant growth can change biodiversity of phytoplankton (plant plankton), this reduces dissolved oxygen when the plants decay, leading to increased turbidity and reduction in light, which can lead to anoxia (oxygen depletion) in bottom layers of the water column, resulting in kills of invertebrates and fish. Eutrophication is considered to be one of the fundamental causes of unusual algal blooms - some of which are toxic resulting in fisheries closures and loss of income to shellfisheries in particular (see Chapter 6).

Algal blooms consist of a variety of phytoplankton. An excessive growth of certain species can cause toxic algal blooms resulting in Paralytic Shellfish Poisoning (PSP), Diarrhoetic Shellfish Poisoning (DSP) and Amnesic Shellfish Poisoning (ASP) in humans who consume contaminated shellfish. The incidences of humans dying in the UK from this type of poisoning is however very rare.

Shellfish producers in particular suffer financial loss as a result of sewage pollution in production areas. Fishermen have also had to remove sanitary waste from fish catches in areas where sewage treatment is inadequate, but a major investment programme in the UK is steadily reducing the number of raw sewage outfalls discharging to coastal waters.

Polycyclic Aromatic Hydrocarbons (PAHs), associated with oil pollution, combustion of fossil fuels and industrial effluent are ubiquitous in the marine environment. PAHs are hydrophobic and are therefore attracted to suspended particles. For this reason PAHs are found in high concentrations in seabed sediments common around oil production and industrial areas. Because of their life-style (see Chapter 1) flat fish species - plaice and dab - are particularly vulnerable to the affects of PAHs. PAHs can cause skin lesions and suppress the immune systems of fish living in contaminated sediment. Due to their hydrophobicity PAHs are also concentrated in the very upper surface layer of the sea – the microlayer – where their toxicity to aquatic life is enhanced when the fauna are also exposed to ultraviolet (UV) light from sunlight. The reaction between PAHs and UV (phototoxicity) increases mortality to larval stages of common European fish and invertebrates, species such as turbot and lobster, which live in the surface layers of the sea during that part of their life-cycle. Commercially harvested fish and shellfish that are contaminated with oil have a tainted flavour and show increased incidence of fin rot and skin lesions. Shellfish and fish contaminated in this way are rejected as unfit for human consumption.

Hazardous substances can affect marine life at every trophic level. The impacts on species biology are very complex and poorly understood although some effects, such as imposex in dogwhelks, are well documented. Imposex is the development of male genitalia in female whelks as a result of exposure to the antifoulant tributyltin (TBT). Antifoulants are used on the hulls of ships and smaller boats to inhibit the growth of marine plants and animals which increases hull resistance. This reduces the speed of the vessel through the water increasing fuel consumption. Oysters can exhibit shell thickening as a result of exposure to TBT. Over 100 species of molluscs are known to have been adversely affected by TBT, and in at least some cases it has been shown that imposex has led to population declines and sometimes total disappearance of species, due to its adverse effect on their ability to reproduce.

Experiments using TBT on human tissue have shown that hormone disruption can occur in the same way as it does with molluscs. The concentrations of TBT at which disrupted hormone function is observed, has raised concerns about the potential risks to human populations that consume large (i.e. in excess of Recommended Daily Allowances) quantities of fish.

On the basis of scientific advice the use of TBT in the UK on vessels including yachts, under 25 m, and fish cages was banned several years ago. From 2003 the application of TBT will be banned on all vessels, and from 2008 its presence on hulls will be banned. Restrictions on the use of TBT have led however to the use of other toxic biocides in anti-fouling paints. There are environmentally-friendly alternatives to biocides in the form of smooth lubricant films which prohibit the attachment of juvenile fouling organisms such as barnacles and macro algae.

Organochlorines are hazardous substances containing chemically combined chlorine and carbon. They do not occur naturally and are the result of industrial chemical activity. Most are toxic, persistent and tend to bioaccumulate in the environment. These qualities make them arguably the most dangerous group of chemicals to which natural systems can be exposed.

Polychlorinated biphenyls (PCBs), dioxins and chloroflurocarbons (CFCs) are examples of organochlorine chemicals and are associated with, amongst other problems, reproductive deformities in marine mammals, population crashes, deformities in birds and fish and depletion of atmospheric ozone. Dioxins and PCBs are known to bioaccumulate in fat and fatty tissues and be biomagnified through the food chain. The main route for exposure to these compounds is through the consumption of fatty foods, such as milk and milk products, meat and fish. Thus, fish oils (liver and body oils) are potentially a source of exposure to dioxins and PCBs.

Although the production and use of PCBs is now banned in many countries they are persistent chemicals. However the levels of PCBs and dioxins in the environment are in decline and all recognised advice (Food Standards Agency (FSA) see Chapter 5) states that the health benefits derived form eating fish oils far out weigh any possible negative effects. Maximum levels for dioxins in foodstuffs (including fish) are set out in an EC Council Regulation which comes into force on 1st July 2002.

Metals like chlorinated hydrocarbons (PCBs) are conservative pollutants i.e. unlike organic wastes (oil and sewage) they are not subject to bacterial decay. They are permanent additions to the marine environment and can accumulate in animal tissue. Mercury, cadmium, copper, lead and zinc are of particular concern for marine organisms. Most mercury in our diets comes from fish. However, an individual would need to consume more than 3 kg of fish per week in order to exceed the tolerable weekly intakes recommended by the World Health Organisation (WHO) and the Food and Agriculture Organisation (FAO) - even people eating fish from heavily contaminated estuaries such as the Mersey, Rhine or Elbe are not considered to be at risk.

Climate change

The effect of climate change on fish stocks is of increasing concern to fishery managers. Healthy fish stocks rely on the recruitment of young fish to the parent stock. In commercial terms, recruitment is defined as the age that young fish enter the fishery and become accessible to fishing gears. Recruitment, and thus the future size of a fish stock, depends on a number of factors including the temperature of the sea. It has been suggested that warming of the North Sea is a contributing factor to reductions in levels of North Sea cod (a cold-water or boreal species) recruitment and reduced spawning stock size.

For warm-water species however the picture is rather different. Increasingly rare or hitherto unusual fish are being captured in UK waters. In particular, sightings of members of the family *Sparidae* (sea breams) and *Carangidae* (jacks, pompanos and scads or horse mackerels) are becoming more common.

Sightings of rare or unusual fish in UK waters can be reported to the National Marine Aquarium at Plymouth (see Appendix 1) who are building a database of sightings.

Other positive effects associated with climate change or global warming are longer breeding periods and faster growth rates for some species.

Changes in species distribution and reproductive success mediated through environmental change are usually difficult to identify or separate from the direct effects of fishing. However, whilst it is not possible to directly control environmental factors such as sea temperature, it is possible to directly control the effects of overfishing on spawning stock size by reducing fishing pressure on stocks.

Chapter Eight
Environmental Issues

Introduction

The effects of fishing on fish stocks was evident more than a 100 years ago and in 1902 the International Council for the Exploration of the Sea (ICES) (see Chapter 6) was established to investigate, amongst other things, the destruction of 'small' plaice in the North Sea.

Today commercial fishing is synonymous with overfishing, by-catch, stock depletion and overcapacity and there is now universal agreement amongst fisheries managers that current management regimes have failed to achieve sustainable exploitation of our stocks.

The Food and Agricultural Organisation (FAO) report that nearly 70% of the world's fish stocks are now fully or over-fished or depleted. (Source FAO 2000)

Impacts of fishing

The impact of fishing on the marine environment is an issue of growing global concern. Fishing impacts upon the wider marine environment produce direct and indirect effects. Although the most evident and direct impact of fishing is fishing mortality and the removal of living organisms or biomass from the marine ecosystem, other impacts associated with commercial fishing include the impact of fishing gears on the seabed and the incidental capture, or by-catch, and mortality of marine mammals, sharks, turtles and birds (see Table 1).

Overfishing

There are two types of overfishing – growth and recruitment overfishing. Growth overfishing is where fish are harvested too early in their life. This occurs most often for demersal species. North Sea cod, whiting and haddock are currently overfished in this way, with virtually no cod in the North Sea aged more than 4 years old (cod only begin to breed at between 4 and 5 years old). Recruitment overfishing occurs when too many of the large, sexually mature fish in a population are captured and there are insufficient adults to maintain the stock. Pelagic species such as anchovy and herring, and species with low reproductive capacity such as marine mammals and elasmobranch (sharks and rays) species, are particularly prone to this type of overfishing.

Table 1: Summary of effects of fishing in the marine environment

- Removal of biomass and overfishing of target species leading to stock depletion
- Physical impact of fishing gears on the seabed - heavy trawling disturbs the seabed, changing the abundance and community structure of mainly demersal and benthic species
- Mortality of by-catch and non-target species such as marine mammals, sharks, turtles, birds and juvenile fish which are often discarded
- Changes in age and size composition of fish populations (recruitment and growth overfishing)
- Changes to marine food webs caused by removal of predators (often at or close to the top of the food-chain) and prey species (often at or close to the base of the food-chain)
- Introduction of fishing-related debris to the marine environment such as lost nets which can continue to fish – 'ghost fishing'

Biodiversity

The oceans, once thought to be less biologically diverse than the land, are now known to be more diverse – 33 of the 34 major categories of animals (phyla) are represented at sea, compared to only 15 on land. The variety of life or biodiversity of our oceans is important for many reasons, including its importance in supporting commercial fish stocks and the food chains and habitats upon which fish and other species rely. Far from being inexhaustible, much of the life of the sea is being pushed close to its limits. Overfishing is now widely acknowledged as the greatest single threat to marine biodiversity. Furthermore, a recent study suggests that ecological extinctions caused by overfishing precedes all other human disturbances to coastal ecosystems including pollution, degradation of water quality and climate change!

There are some 1.8 million known species in the world although the estimated number of species is much higher. In the last 500 years, human activity has forced 816 species to extinction (in the wild). With the current rate of species extinction, estimated to be between 1,000 and 10,000 times higher than the natural rate, many species are being lost before they are even discovered!

To highlight the impact of man's activities on natural resources and to ensure their sustainable use, organisations such as the World Conservation Union (IUCN) and Agreements such as the Convention on International Trade in Endangered Species of Wild Fauna and Flora (CITES) were founded.

IUCN - The World Conservation Union – founded in 1948 brings together States, government agencies and a diverse range of non-governmental organisations in a unique world partnership to ensure the sustainable and equitable use of natural resources.

Every 4 years, IUCN publishes a 'Red List' - an inventory of the current global conservation status of plant and animal species - to raise awareness of species threatened with extinction and promote their conservation. Scientific criteria are used to classify species into one of eight categories: Extinct, Extinct in the Wild, Critically Endangered, Endangered, Vulnerable, Lower Risk, Data Deficient and Not Evaluated.

A total of 11,046 species of plants and animals were listed as threatened in 2000. All face a high risk of extinction in the near future, in almost all cases as a result of human activity. Of the total number (1,267) of fish assessed by IUCN, 284 (22%) are marine. Of these 163 (57%) are assessed as threatened i.e. Critically Endangered, Endangered or Vulnerable. Listed marine species include swordfish, Atlantic cod and halibut, sturgeon, haddock and all tuna species except yellowfin and skipjack. 16 species of albatross are now listed as threatened compared to 3 in 1996, due to the impact of long-line fisheries for Patagonian toothfish, squid and tuna.

CITES is an international agreement between governments, in effect since 1975. Its aim is to ensure that international trade in specimens of wild animals and plants does not threaten their survival. Annually, international wildlife trade is estimated to be worth billions of dollars and to include millions of plant and animal specimens. Levels of exploitation of some animal and plant species are high and the trade

Spider Crab

in them, together with other factors, such as habitat loss, is capable of heavily depleting their populations and even bringing some species close to extinction.

Appendices I, II and III to the Convention list species afforded different levels of protection from over-exploitation. Appendix I lists the most endangered species i.e. those threatened with extinction and generally prohibits their commercial international trade. Appendix II regulates trade in species not threatened with extinction, but which may become threatened if trade goes unregulated and Appendix III regulates trade in species already protected at a national level. All Sturgeons (*Acipenseriformes spp.*), fished for meat and caviar, are listed in Appendix II and the short-nosed sturgeon (*A. brevirostrum*) and European sturgeon (*A. sturio*) are Appendix I listed.

Table 2: Marine species on the IUCN 'Red List' and the CITES Appendices
(Source: Worldwatch 1999)

Species	IUCN Red List	CITES Appendix 1	CITES Appendix 11
Whales, dolphins	13	22	All cetaceans
Marine otters	1	1	1
Seals, sea lions	12	3	9
Sirenians (manatees & dugongs)	3	3	1
Birds	61	4	1
Reptiles (sea turtles)	7	7	1
Fish	163	2	-
Molluscs	10	-	10
Coral	2	-	All stony and black corals

IUU Fishing

Illegal, unreported and unregulated (IUU) fishing is found in all capture fisheries, irrespective of location, size or method, and has been identified as a major fisheries management issue. If unchecked it serves to undermine management initiatives implemented to protect stocks from over exploitation. In extreme cases, IUU can lead to the collapse of a fishery, or seriously affect efforts to rebuild fish stocks that have been depleted. According to FAO, IUU fishing can account for up to 30% of catches.

Among the species being wiped out by 'pirate' boats is the Chilean seabass or Patagonian toothfish. It is the illegal capture of this species, worth an estimated £300 million annually, that is largely responsible for the huge number of albatross killed every year in long-line fisheries (see below). Illegal capture or poaching of sturgeon caviar in the Caspian Sea is also driving stocks of five species, including beluga, the most sought after for its eggs, to extinction. In the UK illegal or 'black' landings of over-quota or non-quota fish serves to undermine management conservation initiatives and depress market prices.

Table 3: Species sold in UK Supermarkets*, considered by MCS to be sensitive to over-exploitation and therefore unsustainable

Supermarket	Sensitive or unsustainable species sold	Species NOT sold on basis of sustainability	Comments
ASDA	Shark (Mako); swordfish; marlin; Atlantic halibut; ling; red snapper; monkfish; Antarctic or Chilean seabass; seabass; hake.	No information	Mako shark not IUCN listed.
Marks & Spencer	Swordfish; Atlantic halibut; monkfish; bigeye tuna.	Blue ling; orange roughy; Chilean seabass; blue or common skate; bluefin tuna; N Sea cod; European hake.	All fresh cod is line caught and not from N Sea; swordfish from Indian & Pacific Ocean; hake from S Africa.
Safeway	Grouper; Atlantic halibut; ling; monkfish; seabass; shark; snapper; swordfish; tuna; scabbardfish; European hake.	Whitebait	Groupers and scabbard fish sold on very limited distribution.
Somerfield	Monkfish	None	Monkfish from SW Peninsula.
Tesco	Marlin	Chilean seabass; shark inc. tope; orange roughy; Whitebait.	Marlin is black marlin from the Indian Ocean.
Waitrose	Orange roughy; swordfish; Chilean seabass; Atlantic halibut; marlin; seabass	North sea cod and haddock; European hake; common skate; black marlin; wild Atlantic salmon; shark; Atlantic swordfish; Bluefin tuna; Beluga, Oscietra & Sevruga caviar; fresh plaice not sold during spawning season.	Orange roughy & Chilean seabass from quota controlled fisheries only; all fresh and frozen cod & haddock is line caught from Icelandic waters; Atlantic halibut is farmed or line caught; striped blue marlin taken as by-catch in long-line fishery for tuna; hake is line caught from S Africa; swordfish line caught in Pacific & Indian Oceans; sea bass line caught.

* all major supermarkets were invited to submit information for the compilation of this table. Table compiled from information received.

In addition, Atlantic cod, haddock, skate (and/or ray) and dogfish are sold by most supermarkets. All of these species are either IUCN listed and/or vulnerable to exploitation because of their biological or life history characteristics.

NB: Many, if not all, of the species highlighted above as sensitive to over-exploitation are widely available from most independent fishmongers depending on their sourcing policy.

Impacts on marine species

Discarding

The practice of discarding or throwing away fish for legislative or economic reasons, creates enormous problems for managing mixed, typically demersal fisheries. From as early as 1960 it was known that about 30% by weight and 50% by number of haddock caught in the North Sea were being discarded. Globally it is estimated that 27 million tonnes (35% of targeted fish) is discarded annually. The highest discard rates occur in prawn and shrimp fisheries where discards can be as high as 10 times the amount of catch landed.

In deep-water fisheries, the shape of many species – large bulbous head and elongate bodies – means that trawl nets, more suited to fishing in shallower water, are likely to retain a higher proportion of juvenile fish and species of little commercial interest. In some fisheries discard rates (by weight) have been estimated to be almost equal to the total amount of fish landed. For example, species known as 'smooth heads' (*Alepocephalus spp*) are unmarketable because of their high water content and are discarded in large quantities. The indiscriminate removal of predator and/or prey species in this way is likely to affect complex food-webs in the marine environment.

Fish and other marine life are discarded for a number of reasons:

- Legislative reasons - fish may be either non-quota or over-quota species
- 'High grading' - the commercial practice of discarding less valuable fish in an attempt to maximise the marketable value of the catch
- Fish less than the legal minimum landing size i.e. juveniles
- Non target species or by-catch which may include species other than fish, such as marine mammals, turtles, seabirds and a great diversity of invertebrates
- Species for which no market exists

By-catch

One of the major problems associated with most types of fishing gear is that it has an incidental or by-catch of non-target species. Depending on the fishery, this may include other commercial and non-commercial fish, seabirds, turtles, sharks and marine mammals such as dolphin, porpoise and sea lions, as well as many species of invertebrates such as starfish, urchins and molluscs etc.

Harbour porpoise entangled in fishing net

Seabirds

Although fishing has had a positive effect on some seabird populations, notably gannets and fulmars, through provision of additional food from discarding of offal and fish, the survival of many species is threatened by fishing. Seabirds, swimming and diving species in particular, can become entangled and drown in fishing gears.

Long-lining poses the greatest threat to seabirds. It is estimated that each year around 40,000 albatross, the world's biggest seabird, die in the Southern Ocean and 250,000 seabirds worldwide die as a result of the long-lining industry.

Ten out of 14 species of albatross are found in the Southern Ocean where they are being killed in huge numbers by commercial long lines trailing thousands of baited hooks for species such as southern bluefin tuna and Patagonian toothfish (Chilean seabass). The birds swallow the baited hooks and are then dragged under the water and drowned.

In the Northern Hemisphere it is estimated that between 50,000 and 100,000 fulmars die annually through being hooked by long-liners operated by Norwegian, Icelandic and Faroese fleets to the north and west of Britain, targeting species such as cod and haddock. Set-nets are also a threat to diving birds because they are not seen before the birds dive into them and become entangled.

Turtles

All of the world's seven marine turtle species are now endangered or vulnerable to extinction. Five species have been recorded in UK waters including the leatherback turtle, widely considered to be native to the UK. Fishing is widely held as the most significant threat to marine turtles in the world today. Hundreds of thousands become entangled and die in fishing gear every year. At one time about 55,000 turtles drowned each year in shrimp nets in the USA alone and today US shrimp trawlers are required by law to fit a Turtle Excluder Device (TED) (see below). Long-line fisheries for swordfish and tuna may catch turtles, as they often use squid, which is a favoured prey of some turtles, as bait. At least 20,000 turtles, primarily loggerheads, are caught every year on long-lines targeting swordfish in the Mediterranean, with mortality estimated between 15-50%.

In UK waters little is known about turtle-fishery interactions. Since 1980 there has been approximately five turtle entanglements recorded per year in UK waters. Of these over 40% involve leatherbacks entangled in buoy ropes for bottom-set gear with a recorded mortality of 61%. The Marine Conservation Society Turtle Conservation Programme

Baby turtle

aunched in 2001 is assessing the causes and impacts of turtle-fishery interactions 'n UK waters and working with the fishing ndustry to develop measures to reduce turtle by-catch.

Pollack

Sharks

Sharks are taken as by-catch in long-line, purse-seine and drift net fisheries for tuna. They are also targeted for their fins, which are a valuable commodity in the Far East for shark fin soup. Often, the dorsal fin is removed whilst the animal is alive and then the rest of the body is discarded or returned to the sea, minus its fins. In 1999, Hong Kong imported nearly 7,000 tonnes of shark fin, representing more than 50 million sharks, about half of the world's fin trade. By comparison Europe imports in the region of 13 million fins. By far the leading exporter of fins to Hong Kong is Spain. The US has already banned shark finning in its waters and a ban throughout the European Union is now being called for.

Marine mammals

A wide variety of interactions occur between marine mammals and fisheries. Catch rates of harbour porpoise are generally highest in set or fixed gill-nets and dolphin deaths highest in drift, purse-seine, pelagic and mid-water pair trawl nets (see Chapter 4 for descriptions of fishing gears).

Gill-net fisheries are responsible for unacceptable levels of harbour porpoise by-catch. For example, in bottom set gill-net fisheries in the Celtic Sea, it has been estimated that 2,200 harbour porpoise, representing 6% of the population, are killed every year by UK and Irish fishermen. Mortality is likely to be less now since some set-net fleets have been reduced by as much as 80%.

In Danish set-net fisheries in the North Sea an estimated 4% of the population of harbour porpoise is removed every year. However, the voluntary use of 'pingers' (see below) in this fishery is reported to have reduced levels of by-catch.

Two to three thousand common dolphins are estimated to die in mid-water pair trawl fisheries for seabass and other species in UK and EU waters every year.

Capture of marine mammals in fishing nets represents a very significant welfare problem. Animals can remain conscious for some time while struggling in the net, causing suffering and injuries such as skin lacerations and broken teeth and bones, before dying of suffocation.

> The International Whaling Commission (IWC) has concluded that by-catch levels of more than 1% of a population should raise concern for long-term sustainability and require immediate action

Despite a global moratorium on large-scale drift nets (nets exceeding 2.5 kms in length), introduced in 1992, problems still exist. For example, drift-net fisheries in the Mediterranean for swordfish and albacore tuna pose a particular threat to striped dolphins. An EU-wide ban on all drift nets is due to be introduced from January 2002. The ban will apply to fisheries such as tuna, shark and swordfish in all EU waters except the Baltic and to all EU vessels on the high seas. Fishermen are, however, considering challenging the ban if 'pingers' are found to be successful in deterring marine mammals from entanglement.

Mitigating measures

The amount of by-catch and thus the rate of discarding may be significantly reduced by increasing the selectivity of the fishing method.

For example, in trawl fisheries, devices known as separator trawls which exploit behavioural differences between fish species, can be used to segregate cod and plaice into the lower net compartment, whilst haddock are taken

Day old kittiwake chick

in the upper compartment. The mesh size for the two compartments can be altered according to the size of the adult fish being targeted. Insertion of square mesh panels also improves the selectivity of the net because square meshes, unlike the traditional diamond shape meshes, do not close when the net is towed. Discarding of immature fish may also be reduced by increasing the basic mesh size of fishing nets.

Mesh sizes for towed nets are laid down in a Council Regulation on technical measures (EC) No 850/98, in which target species are designated, in increasing adult body size, against allowable mesh size ranges, such that the larger bodied fish and shellfish species are only allowed to be landed as a limited percentage by-catch within the total catch, using a mesh size appropriate to smaller species. Thus, sprat, Norway pout, anchovy etc. are allowed to be taken with meshes of 16-32 mm; mackerel, herring and other small pelagic fish with 32-54 mm; sole, hake, bass etc. with 80-99 mm, and cod and other larger species may not be targeted with meshes under 120 mm. A similar regime is in place for fixed nets, and there are variations by sea area. This regulation is actively being amended and refined, especially given the need to build technical measures into the recovery plans for cod and hake fisheries.

Turtles can be excluded from trawl nets by fitting solid grids of various kinds into the net. The Turtle Excluder Device (TED) consists of a metal frame, or hinged door system, which deflects turtles out of a webbing flap or 'trap door' in the bottom of the net. The target species, usually shrimp or prawn, pass through the grid into the cod-end. Ongoing research in the Mediterranean is currently evaluating the impact of alternative types of long-line gear on marine turtle

Redfish catch

by-catch. For example, hook size and shape and branch or snood length.

Marine mammals

A number of techniques have been developed to reduce dolphin mortality in purse seine net fisheries. For example, the use of fine mesh panels near the corkline to prevent entanglement; 'backing down' the vessel after the net is set, to force an end of the corkline under water so that the dolphins escape above it; and sending crewmen into the water to shepherd the animals to freedom.

Nephrops or Dublin Bay prawn

Research into the use and effectiveness of underwater acoustic devices or beacons known as 'pingers' to deter entanglement has also been carried out. The beacons are attached to the fishing net and send out an acoustic signal that alerts cetaceans to the presence of a net thus helping them avoid it. Conservationists are concerned however that widespread use of pingers, to the exclusion of other measures, might cause animals to become habituated to the noise or scare them from important habitat. Acoustically reflective nets have also been developed and tested in the USA recently, with promising results.

Efforts to address by-catch problems in other countries such as the USA and New Zealand are underpinned by targeted legislation and a legal framework. In the USA, commercial fisheries are monitored and Take Reduction Plans (TRPs) have been devised to reduce by-catch levels. TRPs include observer monitoring, area closures and reducing the size of fisheries in which by-catch is problematic.

Seabirds

A range of measures designed to reduce the numbers of seabirds killed by long-lines are now being considered. In particular, research is being conducted into how to best lay long-lines to avoid incidental capture. A reduction in the number of hooks used and seabird deterrent devices to discourage birds from scavenging baited hooks has resulted in reductions to seabird mortality. Although the demersal long-line fishery for Patagonian toothfish uses mitigation measures to reduce seabird by-catch in CCAMLR waters, the much larger IUU fishery for this species was estimated to kill up to 140,000 seabirds (mainly albatross and white-chinned petrels) in 1997.

Competition for fish

Fisheries may compete with other species for the same target species or prey, leading to modifications in predator-prey relationships and changes in marine food chains.

Industrial fisheries - those fisheries targeting species such as sandeel and blue whiting for non-human consumption - are of particular concern because species near the base of the food chain are removed in vast quantities. The industrial fishery for sandeel was implicated in the deaths of thousands of young seabirds, especially puffins and kittiwakes, in Shetland in the 1980s and more recently with the decline of breeding success in kittiwake gulls in the Firth of Forth, Scotland. Kittiwakes feed almost exclusively on sandeel and are therefore particularly sensitive to any changes, natural or otherwise, in their availability in surface waters. The industrial fishery for the lesser sandeel is currently the largest single-species fishery in the North Sea and accounts for over 50% by weight of total fish landings.

Thornback Ray

Whales and seals in particular are perceived by some fishermen to be in competition with man for commercially important fish stocks. This has been used as an argument to initiate seal culls and strengthen arguments for the reintroduction of widespread commercial whaling.

Pro-whaling nations (Japan, Norway and Iceland) blame the decline in commercial fish catches on the presence of marine mammals. For example, Japan maintains that whales eat four times the world catch and that competition between fisheries and whales is increasing. Iceland argues that the yield of Icelandic cod could be increased by 20% once whaling recommences. There is little scientific evidence to support these arguments, as the whales' diet largely comprises species such as krill, crustaceans and cephalopods (squid and cuttlefish) at the base of the food chain. There is however strong scientific evidence linking overfishing and a corresponding decline in commercial fish, marine mammal, shark and bird populations.

Iceland's economy relies very heavily on its fisheries. In 1999, a resolution was passed in the Althings (home to the Icelandic Government) to recommence hunting of minke, sei and fin whales. Although no agreement has yet been reached, Iceland has applied to rejoin the IWC and CITES in an attempt to reduce the protection of these species and reopen trade in whale meat. A budget has also been approved by the Icelandic Government of $270,000 to campaign internationally for a return to commercial whaling.

Many fishermen's organisations in the UK and Ireland are calling for a seal cull. They claim that increasing seal populations - grey seal populations are reported to be increasing by 6% per year - are eating too much fish depriving them of valuable income. There are an estimated 120,000 grey seals (37% of world population) and 33 - 35,000 common seals (5% of world population) in British waters, with over 90% of each species found in Scotland. Scientists from the Sea Mammal Research Unit at St Andrews University, Scotland, have recently warned that a seal cull could cause an irreversible decline in seal populations and are further investigating the diet of seals to determine their impact on commercial fish stocks.

Pouting

Although protected by the Conservation of Seals Act (1970), shooting of seals in the 'vicinity' of fish cages is permitted to protect fish stocks from so called 'rogue' seals. No definition of 'vicinity' is specified in the Act and consequently seals are routinely shot in some areas, many of which are not near fish cages!

Whales, seals, seabirds and other top marine predators form an important and integral part of complex marine food webs. Many, such as marine mammals and sharks are examples of 'keystone' predators i.e. predators that exert an important regulating effect on other species in the community. Their removal could cause untold and irreversible damage to our oceans.

Impacts on the marine environment

Physical impact
The most widely used and energy intensive of all fishing methods is trawling. Its effectiveness relies on traversing a considerable area of seabed or volume of water. This area or volume may be increased by towing more than one net at any time, or by engaging a second vessel, as with pair-trawling. Demersal trawls dragged across the seabed disturb, dig-up and displace, damage or kill animals and habitats in the path of the fishing gear. Some small parts of the North Sea are trawled up to seven times a year. This activity has implications for seabed community structure and for non-target species, such as echinoderms (starfish, urchins and brittlestars) and immature fish, that are routinely captured in these types of fishery.

In the North Atlantic, unique cold-water coral (*Lophelia pertusa*) formations, known as the Darwin Mounds, are being wrecked by deep-water trawling. Apart from the obvious damage to coral reefs little is known about the long-term effects of trawling on the seabed.

Commercial fish species targeted by trawl fisheries include the principle round fish or demersal species, such as cod and haddock, flat fish, such as plaice and sole and deep-water species such as orange roughy and grenadiers. Examples of fisheries that directly affect the seabed world-wide are bottom otter trawling, beam trawling and dredging for bivalve molluscs, such as scallops, clams, mussels and oysters, which takes place world-wide in shallow shelf seas.

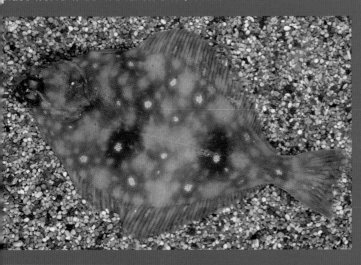

Plaice

Fishing debris

Fishing activity has been identified by the Marine Conservation Society as one of four major sources contributing to litter found on UK beaches. Items such as fishing net, fish boxes and buoys are easily identified and attributable to the fishing industry, accounting for approximately 12% of the total amount of litter found during the annual MCS UK Beachwatch litter surveys.

One of the consequences of fishing-related debris in the marine environment is ghost fishing. This is the term given to the phenomenon whereby nets or pots, lost either because of bad weather, snagging or when towed away by mobile fishing gears, or simply discarded, continue to fish. Little is known about the frequency of net loss or for how long lost gear is likely to fish. Lost nets and pots can continue to fish in the marine environment for several years, although their persistence will be determined by physical factors such as the prevailing conditions of tide and wave action. Nets lost in areas of high

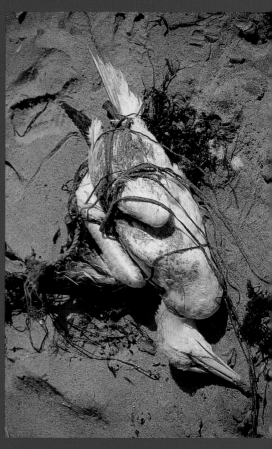

Gannet caught in fishing line

storm activity will be broken up, whereas those lost in deep water in a relatively stable environment, or in circumstances where the gear becomes snagged on rocks, may continue to fish indefinitely. The construction and design of the gear will also determine its ability to fish after loss. For example, pots have a more rigid structure than nets and are likely to maintain a higher capture efficiency for longer. Ghost fishing and other marine debris is responsible for the many deaths of fish, seabirds, turtles, seals and cetaceans world-wide.

Chapter Nine
Social & Economic Issues

Introduction

Fish and its products are some of the most widely traded commodities. In several parts of the world, entire communities live by fishing, their national economies dependent upon the sea and the state of fish stocks.

When fisheries decline there are serious social and economic repercussions for these countries and those communities and individuals depending on them for a livelihood.

> Between 30 and 40% of fish and fish products enter international trade, far more than any other primary commodity.

Overcapacity

The demise of fish stocks is generally attributed to 'too many boats, chasing too few fish'. More specifically it is the way in which fish are caught today that is responsible for over-fishing and declining fish stocks.

Since industrialisation of fisheries in the 1950s fishing boats have become increasingly more efficient at catching fish. Sophisticated sonar and fish-finding equipment, synthetic nets, and other technological advances including the use of GPS (Global Positioning System) satellite imaging and spotter planes to locate fish, have all contributed to overcapacity and the eventual demise of many commercial fish stocks.

> The world fishing fleet possesses more than two and a half times the level of catching power needed to achieve a catch level that would not deplete stocks. The fishing fleet of the European Union, one of the largest fleets in the world, has approximately 40% overcapacity. (Source: www.www.org)

Multi-Annual Guidance Programme (MAGP)

MAGP is one of a number of management tools used within the framework of the European Common Fisheries Policy (CFP) to reduce fishing effort or fishing capacity (other measures include TACS and quotas and technical conservation measures discussed in Chapters 4 and 6). They are designed to establish national fleet reduction targets and monitor progress towards reducing catching capacity throughout the European fleet.

MAGPs were first introduced in 1983 as a measure to achieve a balance on a sustainable basis, between fisheries resources and their exploitation. To date, four programmes have been agreed between 1983 and 2001. The latest programme - MAGP IV (1997-2001) – called for a reduction in catching capacity of 30% for stocks considered to be at risk of collapse and a 20% reduction for over-fished stocks.

In reality these programmes have failed to achieve an effective reduction in catching capacity and have in fact succeeded in increasing fishing pressure in many cases! Generally the oldest and most inefficient boats are the first to be decommissioned or 'scrapped' and in some cases decommissioning or compensation payments are invested in larger and/or more efficient boats. New vessels are more efficient than old ones. Thus although there may be fewer vessels, less tonnage and less power, the catching capacity of the fleet continues to rise as advances in technology keep increasing the unit capacity per tonnage and power – a phenomenon referred to as 'technological creep'.

Another factor contributing to the failure of MAGPs is the use of a 'weighted' formulae to calculate reduction targets. This has resulted in targets falling short of the reduction required to achieve sustainable fishing levels.

So, whilst the number of boats is physically reduced, the capacity or ability of those remaining to remove fish from the sea remains at the same or an increased level. Subsequently, as boat numbers decline, so do the number of jobs and fishermen, as fishing and the benefits attached to it become concentrated in fewer and fewer hands. Loss of jobs in the fishing industry causes erosion of a traditional way of life and the collapse of small and remote communities dependent upon fishing.

Subsidies

Subsidies are also to blame for over-fishing and overcapacity. Between 1970 and 1983 direct subsidies for fishing vessel construction and modernisation, as well as the processing and marketing of fish, contributed to an estimated 64% increase in EU fishing fleet capacity. MAGPs were then introduced in the early 1980s to counteract the surge in increasingly powerful vessels.

> According to FAO estimates US$54 billion was paid in subsidies in 1989 to catch US$70 billion worth of fish.

Subsidies also distort competition and provide incentives to fish above sustainable levels. For example, in Mauritania, high levels of subsidy allow Spanish operators to reduce costs and sell their catches, in this case octopus, on the Japanese market for less than local fishermen. Apart from the social and economic consequences of subsidised fishing, vulnerable stocks of octopus are also being over-exploited.

Subsidies can however help reduce fishing effort and increase gear selectivity by creating economic or financial incentives for fishermen to switch to more environmentally and people friendly methods of fishing.

Atlantic Dawn

'Atlantic Dawn' is one of a new-generation of super-trawlers and was dubbed 'the biggest fishing vessel in the world' when it was launched in September 2000. The vessel, costing 50 million Irish Punts (IEP) was built in Norway with the assistance of a 44 million kroner (£3-4 million) Norwegian boat-yard grant. Irish-owned Atlantic Dawn is one of the largest and potentially the most destructive European-owned fishing vessel.

> Launched in 2000 the Atlantic Dawn is one of a new breed of 'super trawlers'. It is 144 m in length and has the capacity to process 350 tonnes of fish a day and can carry 7,000 tonnes of frozen fish!

Because the size of the vessel clearly contravenes EU attempts to reduce fishing capacity, the Atlantic Dawn is not currently registered as a fishing vessel. Rather it has been registered as a merchant vessel to circumvent the rules! The Irish Government is however applying to the Commission to have it re-registered as an EU fishing vessel. Atlantic Dawn is currently fishing in Mauritanian waters where the EU has just renewed a five-year fisheries agreement at a cost to EU taxpayers of 430 million ECU.

Although Atlantic Dawn is portrayed as a means of feeding hungry people in Africa, it is not perceived in that way by local people. The factory-ship targets, processes and freezes pelagic species such as sardinella, herring, pilchard and anchovy at sea. The fish are caught either by pelagic trawl or purse seining, both of which are highly unselective methods of fishing. The purse seine net is reported to be more than 3,600 feet in circumference and over 550 feet deep – large enough to engulf two London Domes! The huge catches are 'pumped' on board, graded and then frozen in 22 kg blocks.

Artisanal fishermen in Senegal and other West African countries would normally catch these fish when they move into shallower water on their migration along the African coast – in one day the Atlantic Dawn can process as much fish as several large African canoes or 'pirogues' can catch in one good fishing year! Local fishermen also have sophisticated networks to distribute and market their catch locally and in the interior. Both inshore fisheries and the networks and markets to distribute catches are likely to be destroyed by vessels like the Atlantic Dawn catching and landing huge quantities of frozen fish all at once.

Third Country Agreements or 'Cash for Access'

Another solution to the problem of overcapacity within Europe is to 'export' it. In the 1970s many distant-water fishing boats were displaced when countries extended their Exclusive Economic Zones (EEZs) to 200 nautical miles (see Chapter 6). To ensure continuing access to fish in these waters Agreements were made with third countries i.e. non-EU members.

Since 1977, a total of 29 agreements have been made, mainly with African and Indian Ocean countries and countries of the North Atlantic. Countries include Iceland, Greenland, Angola, Mauritius, Senegal, Mauritania and, most recently, Argentina (referred to as 'second generation' agreements) for example. Third Country Agreements permit access to the host country's fish resources, which they themselves are unable to exploit fully, in return for financial compensation.

One third of the CFP budget, just under 300 million Euro, is spent annually on securing access to distant waters. A further 8%, some 80 million Euro, is spent transferring EU vessels to foreign fishing fleets. Distant waters provide 20-25% of fish consumed in the EU, with some 1,300 EU vessels and 20,000 jobs depending upon fisheries agreements. Europe has one of the largest distant water fleets after Russia and Japan.

Livelihoods and fishing communities

In many developing countries such as Senegal and Mauritania there is widespread poverty and often their rich marine resources are the country's only wealth.

Artisanal or small-scale coastal fisheries play an important role in the employment, income security, nutrition and standard of living of many poor populations in these countries. They are also important in that unlike large-scale or commercial fisheries, small-scale fisheries have a cultural rather than a purely commercial value.

> Around 200 million of the world's poorest people depend on fishing for all or part of their livelihood.

The small-scale sector also produces more economic benefits than the industrial one by ensuring that benefits are equitably distributed. It uses less capital and fuel, generally employs more selective fishing gear, is based in rural areas and usually produces more food for the domestic market than for export. Small-scale fishers also have an inherent capacity to switch gears and resources seasonally and to combine fishing with non-fishing activities.

Although they should, fishing agreements do not take account of the economic and environmental impact they have on the coastal communities concerned. Artisanal fisheries are labour-intensive and involve many community and family members in their activities. Women traditionally play key roles in marketing and processing the catch, but may be displaced by modernisation; synthetic nets will be factory made rather than hand-woven; and fish caught by bigger boats will be landed at distant ports rather than on the local beach.

Tens of thousands of jobs in the small-scale sector are being lost because of declining catches and competition from large vessels. Traditional ways of life, which for centuries have been sustained by fishing, are collapsing.

Foreign industrial fleets have been accused of taking more than their legally agreed quotas, of intruding into inshore waters or zones reserved for local boats, and of discarding huge quantities of low value or juvenile fish.

The intensive fishing activities of industrial fishing vessels on vulnerable fish stocks, prone to wide fluctuations, is the cause for much alarm, and unless controlled represents a serious threat to the fish stocks on which coastal livelihoods depend.

In the case of demersal stocks in Senegal and Mauritania, most notably octopus stocks in Mauritania, intensive fishing activities represent a significant threat, and have in the case of the octopus, reduced them to the point of commercial extinction.

An even more serious threat however is the number of small artisanal boats being sunk by foreign trawlers sneaking into inshore zones reserved for local fishermen. In Mauritanian waters nearly 300 fishermen have perished in the last year. (This figure does not include those from neighbouring Senegal who work most of the pirogues but are not registered fishermen). If the trawler responsible is identified the owner will be ordered to pay less than £3,500 compensation, or let off scot-free! Although the EU Agreement was hailed as being of 'mutual benefit' – the Mauritanian Government desperately needs foreign cash to pay the interest on its crippling foreign debts and Europe wants fish - local fishermen's representatives now regard the EU deal as a human and ecological disaster.

International trade in fish
World-wide about a billion people rely on fish as the main source of protein and other essential nutrients (particularly as a source of calcium for mothers and children). Dependence is generally higher in coastal areas than in inland areas.

> *60% of the global fish catch is derived from fisheries in waters of developing countries.*

Most fish traded internationally comes from the waters of developing countries in the southern-hemisphere but is eaten in the north, in developed countries. Here the consumption of fish has increased from 13.2 million tonnes in 1961 to 26.7 million tonnes in 1997, representing a rise in average annual per capita consumption from 19.7 to 27.7 kgs.

Traditionally fish has provided an accessible and low-cost protein. It is essential and critical in the diet of some densely populated countries particularly where the total protein intake level is low. In countries such as Bangladesh, Ghana and Senegal fish contributes more than 50% of the total protein intake.

Developing countries in general depend heavily on primary commodities for their export revenues and foreign exchange earnings. In many cases fish exports have replaced more traditional products like tea and coffee as the main source of foreign exchange earnings. But unlike other commodities, fish, although renewable, is a fragile and limited resource.

Because of foreign fleets and export-driven policies, people in developing countries in the south are eating less fish. About 50% of the total trade in fish and fish products is from developing countries. Imports of fish into Japan, Europe and the USA, the three largest importing blocs, have been consistently growing over the past few years.

The EU is a key player in the international trade in fish – some 60% of the fish consumed in EU Member States is imported, with a significant proportion of this coming from developing countries. As the crisis in waters of developed countries deepens, market demands are placing increasing pressures on fishery resources in waters of the south.

Cornish fishing harbour

Transport and food miles

Apart from the social and economic impacts associated with international trade in fish there are also impacts for the environment as a result of the distance travelled by food.

'Food miles' is the term used to describe the distance food has travelled before it is available to consumers. As a result of the globalisation of food production and trade, food is travelling further than ever before.

Turbot

> *Within the UK, a tonne of food now travels an average distance of 123 km compared to 82 km in 1978*   *(Source: Sustain 1998)*

In 1994 the SAFE Alliance (now called Sustain: the alliance for better food and farming) launched the Food Miles Report, which for the first time illustrated the environmental and social implications of the rapid escalation in the distance our food was travelling, from 'the plough (or the fishing boat) to the plate'.

Relatively cheap fuel makes long-distance transport economically viable and has allowed food production and distribution to become global industries.

As European stocks in waters closer to home become depleted and demand for fish increases, fishers are exploiting more distant waters.

Fish, particularly luxury commodities, such as tiger prawn, tuna, swordfish and more recently cod, is often air freighted to ensure that the freshness and quality of the fish is maintained. Transporting commodities by air, which uses nearly 40 times the amount of fuel that sea transport uses, is now a feature of world trade. Table 1 lists the distances travelled by air, between country of origin and the UK (London), for selected fish products.

Actual 'food miles' will be much higher for each product as, in addition to distance travelled by air, the product also travels by fishing boat from the point of capture to the port of landing; then by road or rail to the airport; from the airport by road or rail to the processor; and finally by road or rail to the retailer where it is purchased by the consumer, who themselves usually travel by road!

Save our fish

Table 1: Distance travelled by air for selected fish products

Species	Miles travelled by air
Australian rock lobster	10,500
Chilean farmed salmon	8,000
Chilean swordfish	8,000
New Zealand hoki	13,000
South African hake	6,800
Thai prawns	7,800

Fair-trade

Fair-trade is an alternative approach to conventional international trade. Fair-trade practices have been designed to encourage more equitable distribution of benefits across the production, trading and consumption system i.e. fair-trade practices are being promoted so that producers and processing workers can take a fair share of the profits generated by the sale of their products. It also ensures that industrialists, investors, traders and consumers pay a fair price for the goods and services from which they benefit.

Fair-trade is about:
- Providing a fair share of the benefits from production for primary producers and processing workers
- Promotion of safe and adequate working conditions
- Promotion of sustainable and /or organic production

Fair-trade Foundation
The Fair-trade Foundation exists to ensure a better deal for marginalised and disadvantaged third world producers. The Foundation awards a consumer label (see Chapter 2) - the Fair-trade mark - to products which meet internationally recognised standards of fair-trade. Consumers can play an important role in improving the social and economic situation for producers of commodities such as tea, coffee, chocolate

and bananas in third-world countries by buying fair-trade products. The Fair-trade mark is the UK's only independent guarantee that products meet standards and are fairly traded.

Fair-trade and fishing
The application of the concept of fair-trade to fisheries is fairly new. India is one of the first countries where an initiative is being undertaken to apply the concept.

Whelk

> *Imagine – fish consumers preferring – fish caught with passive gears – or a situation where the world's seafood eaters actually begin demanding only those fish processed in factories by management which respect the dignity of labour and employ fishworkers on equitable terms. Can we – should we – leave this to the realm of mere imagination?*
>
> Source: Sumudra Report (1994)

Artisanal fishermen, including those from some areas of UK and other European countries, represent some of the most marginalised and disadvantaged people in the world, they live in close contact with their local environment and do not travel long distances to make their catches. Small-scale fishers tend to use static or passive gears or mobile gear which is less powerful and less damaging to the environment. It is the basic nature of these fisheries that has marketing potential to create both social and environmental benefits.

'Eco-labelling' (see Chapter 2) of fisheries products could be developed to provide direct employment and economic benefits to local fishers. This would not only ensure that communities dependent on fishing survived. It would also ensure that marine resources were sustainably exploited and fairly traded.

Awareness is growing in developing countries of the value of properly managed and sustainably exploited fisheries resources and of the potential for these resources to provide for increased levels of employment, improved food security and local and national economic development. As a result, questions are now being raised about the sustainability and desirability of the current levels of fishing access made available to EU and other vessels.

Fishworkers welfare

Artisanal coastal fishermen in developing countries are increasingly organising themselves to challenge competition from industrial fleets fishing in their waters. It is through these organisations that the interests of artisanal fishworkers and the sustainable exploitation of coastal resources are represented.

World Forum of Fishworkers and Fish Harvesters
In October 1995 an international committee was formed in Quebec City, Canada to oppose the world-wide depletion of fish stocks. In a statement it expressed 'deep concern over the reckless plunder of the seas by the large, industrialised fleets of the

world, leading to a substantial depletion of fish stocks and endangering the food security of millions of people'.

The Forum has condemned the Governments who have sought to find short-term solutions to their national problems by exporting over-capacity as unethical and leading to further destruction of fish stocks and the replacement of small-scale fish harvesters.

Whiting

International Collective in Support of Fishworkers (ICSF)

ICSF was founded in 1986 in India. It is an international NGO that works on issues that concern fish workers the world over, but with an emphasis on countries of the south. It produces a regular report-Sumudra, and is a founder member of the Coalition for Fair Fisheries Agreements. ICSF has Members in more than 17 countries with about 60% of these from Asia, Africa and Latin America. ICSF's approach to fisheries is from a community and livelihoods perspective and believes that sustaining fisheries is as much about conserving fish stocks as it is about sustaining livelihoods and economic activities in coastal communities with access to few alternative resources.

Coalition for Fair Fisheries Agreements (CFFA)

CFFA is an association of European NGOs concerned about the developmental and environmental aspects of EU third country fishing agreements. CFFA argue that such agreements should not be regarded as purely commercial in nature. Rather the main priorities should be fostering longer-term sustainable, social and economic development in the fisheries sector, and protecting the marine environment. The overall aim of CFFA activities is therefore to promote a re-evaluation of EU Fisheries Agreement policy and practice with a view to creating more sustainable patterns of exploitation, which contribute to the wider social and economic development of coastal countries.

Other organisations such as Oxfam exist to improve the working conditions and living standards of people all over the world.

Ethical Trade Initiative (ETI)

ETI is an alliance of companies, NGOs and trade union organisations whose aim is to help make substantial improvements to the lives of working people around the world. It aims to develop and encourage the use of a widely endorsed set of standards or Code of Labour Practice which will enable companies to work together with organisations outside the corporate sector to improve labour conditions around the world. The Code is based on International Labour Organisation (ILO) Conventions and covers aspects such as working conditions, wage levels and child labour.

Fishing harbour, Ghana, West Africa

Appendices

Appendix 1 - Contacts

Supermarkets

ASDA Stores
Asda House
South Bank
Great Wilson Street
Leeds LS11 5AD
Tel: 0113 2435435
www.asda.co.uk

CO-OP
PO Box 53
New Century House
Manchester M60 4ES
Tel: 0161 8341212
www.co-op.co.uk

Iceland Frozen Foods
Second Avenue
Deeside Industrial Park
Deeside
Flintshire CH5 2NW
Tel: 01244 830 100
www.iceland.co.uk

Marks & Spencer
Michael House
47-67 Baker Street
London W1A 1DN
Tel: 020 7935 4422
www.marksandspencer.com

Safeways Supermarket
6 Millington Road
Hayes
Middlesex UB3 4AY
Tel: 0208 848 8744
www.safeway.co.uk

Sainsbury Supermarkets
Stamford House
Stamford Street
London SE1 9LL
Tel: 020 7695 8602
www.sainsburys.co.uk

Somerfield
Somerfield House
Hawkfield Business Park
Whitchurch Lane
Bristol BS14 0TJ
Tel: 0117 9359359
www.somerfield.plc.uk

Tesco Stores
Tesco House
PO Box 18
Delamare Road
Chesthunt, Waltham Cross
Hertfordshire EN8 9SL
Tel: 01992 632222
www.tesco.com

Waitrose
Doncastle Road
Southern Industrial Area
Bracknell
Berkshire RG12 8YA
Tel: 01344 424680
www.waitrose.com

W Morrison Supermarkets
Wakefield 41 Industrial Park
Wakefield
West Yorkshire WF2 0XF
Tel: 01924 870000
www.morrisons.plc.uk

Seafood suppliers and restaurants

Birds Eye Wall's Ltd
Station Avenue
Walton-on-Thames
KT12 1NT
Tel: 01932 263 000

Dawnfresh Seafoods Ltd
Bothwell Park Industrial Estate
Uddingston
Strathclyde G71 6LS
Tel: 01698 810008

Findus Ltd
Benton Lane
Longbenton
Newcastle-upon-Tyne
NE12 8EF
Tel: 0191 202 1224

Fish! Plc
56 Ayres Street
London SE1 1EU
Tel: 020 7234 3300
www.fishdiner.co.uk

Fisher Foods
Macfish House
Watermill Road
Fraserburgh AB43 9HA
Tel: 01472 263 450
www.fisherfoodsgroup.com

Glenryck (UK) Ltd
PO Box 22
17 Market Place
Henley-on-Thames
RG9 2AA
Tel: 01491 578123

John West Foods Ltd
West House
Bixteth Street
Liverpool L3 9SR
Tel: 0151 236 8771/243 62000

KJ Lovering & Co Ltd
   Kingfisher House
   Mid Street
   South Nutfield RH1 4JY
   Tel: 01737 822655

Loch Duart Ltd
   Badcall Salmon House
   Scourie
   Sutherland IU27 4TH
   Tel: 01971 502451
   www.lochduart.com

Loch Fyne Head Office
   175 Hampton Road
   Twickenham
   TW2 5NG
   Tel: 0208 404 6686
   http://test.loch-fyne.com

Lyons Seafoods Ltd
   Barrow House
   Bishopstrow
   Warminster BA12 9HU
   Tel: 01985 214565

Marr Foods Ltd
   Pinegain House
   Gillet Street
   Hull HU3 4JG
   www.marrfoods.co.uk

Princes Foods
   Royal Liver Building
   Pier Head
   Liverpool L3 1NX
   Tel: 0151 236 9282
   www.princes.co.uk

Ross
   Ross House
   Wickham Road
   Grimsby DN31 3SW
   Customer Service Line
   Tel: 0800 387 266

Royal Greenland Ltd
   Sinclair House
   Cheadle Hulme SK8 5AF
   Tel: 0161 485 8385

Salar Ltd
   Lochcarnan
   South Uist
   Outer Hebrides HS8 5PD
   Tel: 01870 610 324
   www.salar.co.uk

The Seafood Company Ltd
   Devonshire House
   Handcross RH17 6BJ
   Tel: 01444 400 363

Youngs Bluecrest
   Seafood Ltd
   Ross House, Wickham Road
   Grimsby DN31 3SW
   Tel: 01472 585858

Seafood and fishing interest

Association of Sea Fisheries Committees
   24 Wykeham
   Scarborough YO13 9QP
   Tel: 01723 863169

Findlay's Foods Ltd
   CAVI*ART
   60 Sherbourne Street
   Manchester MB 8LR
   Tel: 0161 832 7788
   www.finlaysfoods.co.uk

Frozen at Sea Fillets Association (FASFA)
   PO Box 197
   Hull HU1 2YJ
   Tel: 01482 324024
   www.frozenatseafillets.com

National Federation of Fishermen's Organisations
(NFFO)
   Marsden Road
   Fish Dock
   Grimsby DN31 3SG
   Tel: 01472 352 141
   www.nffo.org.uk

Seafish Industry Authority
(Seafish)
   18 Logie Mill
   Logie Green Road
   Edinburgh EH7 4HG
   Tel: 0131 558 3331
   www.seafish.co.uk

Seafood Scotland
   18 Logie Green
   Edinburgh EH7 4HG
   Tel: 0131 557 9344
   www.seafoodscotland.org

Shellfish Association of Great Britain
   Fishmongers' Hall
   London Bridge
   London EC4R 9EL
   Tel: 020 7283 8305
   www.shellfish.org.uk

Scottish Fishermen's Federation (SFF)
   14 Regent Quay
   Aberdeen AB11 5AE
   Tel: 01224 582 583
   www.sff.co.uk

Scottish Quality Salmon
   Durn
   Isla Road
   Perth PH2 7HG
   Tel: 01738 587000
   www.scottishsalmon.co.uk

Organisations with conservation, marine, fishing and/or consumer interests

Atlantic Salmon Trust Ltd
  Moulin
  Pitlochry PH16 5JQ
  Tel: 01796 473 439
  www.atlanticsalmontrust.org

Bass Anglers Sportfishing Society (BASS)
  www.ukbass.com

Earth Island Institute (EII)
  300 Broadway
  Suite 28
  San Francisco
  CA 94133
  www.earthisland.org

Ethical Consumer Magazine
  Unit 21
  41 Old Birley Street
  Manchester M15 5RF
  Tel: 0161 226 2929
  www.ethicalconsumer.org

European Cetacean Bycatch Campaign (ECBC)
  8 Highgrove Road
  Walderslade
  Chatham ME5 7QE
  Tel: 01634 669 386

Friends of the Earth (Scotland)
  72 Newhaven Street
  Edinburgh EH6 5QG
  Tel: 0131 557 3432
  www.foe-scotland.org.uk

Greenpeace
  Greenpeace House
  1 Canonbury Villas
  London N1 2PN
  Tel: 020 7865 8100
  www.greenpeace.org.uk

International Fund for Animal Welfare (IFAW)
  89 Albert Embankment
  London SE1 7UD
  Tel: 020 7587 6736
  www.ifaw.org

Marine Connection
  PO Box 2404
  London W2 3WG
  Tel: 0207 499 9196
  www.marineconnection.org

Marine Conservation Society (MCS)
  9 Gloucester Road
  Ross-on-Wye HR9 5BU
  Tel: 01989 566017
  www.mcsuk.org

Marine Stewardship Council (MSC)
  119 Altenburg Gardens
  London SW11 1JQ
  Tel: 020 7350 4000
  www.msc.org

National Federation of Sea Anglers (NFSA)
  Hamlyn House
  Mardleway
  Buckfastleigh TQ11 0NS
  Tel: 01364 644 643
  www.nfsa.org.uk

National Marine Aquarium
  UK Marine Fish Recording Scheme
  Rope Walk
  Coxside
  Plymouth PL4 0LF
  Tel: 01752 275216
  www.national-aquarium.co.uk

National Mullet Club
  38 Sackville Road
  Hove BN3 3FB
  Tel: 01273 728 410

Royal Society for the Protection of Birds (RSPB)
  The Lodge, Sandy,
  Bedfordshire
  SG19 2DL
  Tel: 01767 680 551
  www.rspb.org.uk

Royal Society for the Prevention of Cruelty to Animals (RSPCA)
  Wilberforce Way
  Southwater
  Horsham
  Tel: 0870 010 1181
  www.rspca.org.uk

Sea Anglers Conservation Network (SACN)
  Anglers Net
  PO Box 309
  Woolpit
  Bury-St-Edmunds IP30 9WA
  www.anglersnet.co.uk/sacn

Seal Conservation Society
  25 Lerwick Road
  Aberdeen AB16 6RF
  Tel: 01224 696 362
  www.pinnipeds.fsnet.co.uk

Shark Trust
  National Marine Aquarium
  Rope Walk
  Coxside
  Plymouth PL4 0LF
  Tel: 01752 672 008

Soil Association
  Bristol House
  40-56 Victoria Street
  Bristol BS1 6BY
  Tel: 0117 929 0661
  www.soilassociation.org

Sustain – Alliance for better Food & Farming
94 White Lion Street
London N1 9PF
Tel: 0207 8371 228
www.sustainweb.org

Whale & Dolphin Conservation Society
Alexander House
James Street West
Bath BA1 2BT
Tel: 01225 334511
www.wdcs.org

World Conservation Union (IUCN)
219c Huntingdon Road
Cambridge
CB3 0DL
Tel: 01223 277 966
www.iucn.org

World Wide Fund for Nature (WWF-UK)
Panda House, Weyside Park
Godalming
Surrey GU7 1XR
Tel: 01483 426 444
www.wwf-uk.org

Government, Government Agencies and Organisations with responsibilities for marine and fisheries management and/or consumer interests

Centre for Environment, Fisheries & Aquaculture Science (CEFAS)
Lowestoft Laboratory
Pakefield Road
Lowestoft NR33 OHT
Tel: 01502 562 244
www.cefas.co.uk

CITES
International Environment House
Chemindes Anemones
CH-1219 Chatelaine
Geneva
Switzerland
www.cites.org

Countryside Council for Wales (CCW)
Plas Penrhos
Fford Penrhos, Bangor,
Gwynedd LL57 2LQ
Tel: 01248 370 444
www.ccw.gov.uk

DEFRA
Nobel House
17 Smith Square
London SW1P 3JR
Tel: 0207 7238 6000
www.defra.gov.uk

English Nature
Northminster House
Peterborough PE1 1UA
Tel: 01733 455 000
www.english-nature.org.uk

Environment Agency
Rio House, Waterside Drive,
Aztec House West, Almondsbury,
Bristol BS12 4UD
Tel: 01454 624 400
www.environment-agency.gov.uk

European Commission
Directorate General
Environment (DGX11) and Fisheries (DGX1V)
Rue de la Loi 200
B-1049, Brussels, Belgium
Tel: 00 32 2299 1111
www.europa.eu

Food and Agriculture Organisation (FAO)
Viale delle Terme di Caracalla, 00100
Rome, Italy
www.fao.org

Food Standards Agency
Aviation House
125 Kingsway
London WC2B 6NH
Tel: 020 7276 8000
www.food.gov.uk

International Council for the Exploration of the Seas (ICES)
Palaegade 2-4
DK-1261, Copenhagen
Denmark
Tel: 00 45 3315 4225
www.ices.dk

Joint Nature Conservation Committee (JNCC)
Monkstone House
City Road
Peterborough PE1 1JY
Tel: 01733 562 626
www.jncc.gov.uk

Marine Laboratory Aberdeen
Fisheries Research Services
PO Box 101
Victoria Road
Aberdeen AB11 9DB
Tel: 01224 876544
www.marlab.ac.uk

National Assembly for Wales
Cardiff Bay
Cardiff CF99 1NA
Tel: 02920 825111
www.wales.gov.uk

Scottish Natural Heritage (SNH)
12 Hope Terrace
Edinburgh EH9 2AS
Tel: 0131 447 4784
www.snh.org.uk

SEERAD
Pentland House
47 Robbs Loan
Edinburgh EH14 1TY
Tel: 0131 556 8400
www.scotland.gov.uk

Appendix 2
Marine Stewardship Council (MSC) Principles & Criteria

At the centre of the MSC is a set of Principles and Criteria for Sustainable Fishing which are used as a standard in a third party, independent and voluntary certification programme. These were developed by means of an extensive, international consultative process through which the views of stakeholders in fisheries were gathered.

These Principles reflect a recognition that a sustainable fishery should be based upon:

- The maintenance and re-establishment of healthy populations of targeted species;
- The maintenance of the integrity of ecosystems;
- The development and maintenance of effective fisheries management systems, taking into account all relevant biological, technological, economic, social, environmental and commercial aspects; and
- Compliance with relevant local and national local laws and standards and international understandings and agreements

The Principles and Criteria are further designed to recognise and emphasise that management efforts are most likely to be successful in accomplishing the goals of conservation and sustainable use of marine resources when there is full co-operation among the full range of fisheries stakeholders, including those who are dependent on fishing for their food and livelihood.

On a voluntary basis, fisheries which conform to these Principles and Criteria will be eligible for certification by independent MSC-accredited certifiers. Fish processors, traders and retailers will be encouraged to make public commitments to purchase fish products only from certified sources. This will allow consumers to select fish products with the confidence that they come from sustainable, well managed sources. It will also benefit the fishers and the fishing industry who depend on the abundance of fish stocks, by providing market incentives to work towards sustainable practices. Fish processors, traders and retailers who buy from certified sustainable sources will in turn benefit from the assurance of continuity of future supply and hence sustainability of their own businesses.

The MSC promotes equal access to its certification programme irrespective of the scale of the fishing operation. The implications of the size, scale, type, location and intensity of the fishery, the uniqueness of the resources and the effects on other ecosystems will be considered in every certification.

The MSC further recognises the need to observe and respect the long-term interests of people dependent on fishing for food and livelihood to the extent that it is consistent with ecological sustainability, and also the importance of fisheries management and operations being conducted in a manner consistent with established local, national, and international rules and standards as well as in compliance with the MSC Principles and Criteria.

Preamble

The following draft Principles & Criteria are intended to guide the efforts of the Marine Stewardship Council towards the development of sustainable fisheries on a global basis. They were developed assuming that a sustainable fishery is defined, for the purposes of MSC certification, as one that is conducted in such a way that:

- it can be continued indefinitely at a reasonable level;
- it maintains and seeks to maximise, ecological health and abundance,
- it maintains the diversity, structure and function of the ecosystem on which it depends as well as the quality of its habitat, minimising the adverse effects that it causes;
- it is managed and operated in a responsible manner, in conformity with local, national and international laws and regulations;
- it maintains present and future economic and social options and benefits;
- it is conducted in a socially and economically fair and responsible manner.

The following principles represent the overarching philosophical basis for this initiative in stewardship of marine resources: the use of market forces to promote behaviour which helps achieve the goal of sustainable fisheries. The Principles form the basis for detailed Criteria which will be used to evaluate each fishery seeking certification under the MSC programme. Although the primary focus is the ecological integrity of world fisheries, the principles also embrace the human and social elements of fisheries. Their successful implementation depends upon a system which is open, fair, based upon the best information available and which incorporates all relevant legal obligations. The certification programme in which these principles will be applied is intended to give any fishery the opportunity to demonstrate its commitment to sustainable fishing and ultimately benefit from this commitment in the market place.

Scope

The scope of the MSC Principles and Criteria relates to marine fisheries activities up to but not beyond the point at which the fish are landed. However, MSC-accredited certifiers may be informed of serious concerns associated with post-landing practices.

The MSC Principles and Criteria apply at this stage only to wildcapture fisheries (including, but not limited to shellfish, crustaceans and cephalopods). Aquaculture and the harvest of other species are not currently included. Issues involving allocation of quotas and access to marine resources are considered to be beyond the scope of these Principles and Criteria.

PRINCIPLE 1

A fishery must be conducted in a manner that does not lead to over-fishing or depletion of the exploited populations and, for those populations that are depleted, the fishery must be conducted in a manner that demonstrably leads to their recovery. :

Intent:

The intent of this principle is to ensure that the productive capacities of resources are maintained at high levels and are not sacrificed in favour of short term interests. Thus, exploited populations would be maintained at high levels of abundance designed to retain their productivity, provide margins of safety for error and uncertainty, and restore and retain their capacities for yields over the long term.

Criteria:

1. The fishery shall be conducted at catch levels that continually maintain the high productivity of the target population(s) and associated ecological community relative to its potential productivity.

2. Where the exploited populations are depleted, the fishery will be executed such that recovery and rebuilding is allowed to occur to a specified level consistent with the precautionary approach and the ability of the populations to produce long-term potential yields within a specified time frame.

3. Fishing is conducted in a manner that does not alter the age or genetic structure or sex composition to a degree that impairs reproductive capacity.

PRINCIPLE 2:

Fishing operations should allow for the maintenance of the structure, productivity, function and diversity of the ecosystem (including habitat and associated dependent and ecologically related species) on which the fishery depends.

Intent:

The intent of this principle is to encourage the management of fisheries from an ecosystem perspective under a system designed to assess and restrain the impacts of the fishery on the ecosystem.

Criteria:

1. The fishery is conducted in a way that maintains natural functional relationships among species and should not lead to trophic cascades or ecosystem state changes.

2. The fishery is conducted in a manner that does not threaten biological diversity at the genetic, species or population levels and avoids or minimises mortality of, or injuries to endangered, threatened or protected species.

3. Where exploited populations are depleted, the fishery will be executed such that recovery and rebuilding is allowed to occur to a specified level within specified time frames, consistent with the precautionary approach and considering the ability of the population to produce long-term potential yields.

PRINCIPLE 3:

The fishery is subject to an effective management system that respects local, national and international laws and standards and incorporates institutional and operational frameworks that require use of the resource to be responsible and sustainable.

Intent:

The intent of this principle is to ensure that there is an institutional and operational framework for implementing Principles 1 and 2, appropriate to the size and scale of the fishery.

A. Management System Criteria:

1. The fishery shall not be conducted under a controversial unilateral exemption to an international agreement.

The management system shall:

2. demonstrate clear long-term objectives consistent with MSC Principles and Criteria and contain a consultative process that is transparent and involves all interested and affected parties so as to consider all relevant

information, including local knowledge. The impact of fishery management decisions on all those who depend on the fishery for their livelihoods, including, but not confined to subsistence, artisinal, and fishing-dependent communities shall be addressed as part of this process;

3. be appropriate to the cultural context, scale and intensity of the fishery - reflecting specific objectives, incorporating operational criteria, containing procedures for implementation and a process for monitoring and evaluating performance and acting on findings;

4. observe the legal and customary rights and long term interests of people dependent on fishing for food and livelihood, in a manner consistent with ecological sustainability;

5. incorporates an appropriate mechanism for the resolution of disputes arising within the system;

6. provide economic and social incentives that contribute to sustainable fishing and shall not operate with subsidies that contribute to unsustainable fishing;

7. act in a timely and adaptive fashion on the basis of the best available information using a precautionary approach particularly when dealing with scientific uncertainty;

8. incorporate a research plan - appropriate to the scale and intensity of the fishery - that addresses the information needs of management and provides for the dissemination of research results to all interested parties in a timely fashion;

9. require that assessments of the biological status of the resource and impacts of the fishery have been and are periodically conducted;

10. specify measures and strategies that demonstrably control the degree of exploitation of the resource, including, but not limited to:

   a. setting catch levels that will maintain the target population and ecological community's high productivity relative to its potential productivity, and account for the non-target species (or size, age, sex) captured and landed in association with, or as a consequence of, fishing for target species;
   b. identifying appropriate fishing methods that minimise adverse impacts on habitat, especially in critical or sensitive zones such as spawning and nursery areas;
   c. providing for the recovery and rebuilding of depleted fish populations to specified levels within specified time frames;

   d. mechanisms in place to limit or close fisheries when designated catch limits are reached;

   e. establishing no-take zones where appropriate;

11. contains appropriate procedures for effective compliance, monitoring, control, surveillance and enforcement which ensure that established limits to exploitation are not exceeded and specifies corrective actions to be taken in the event that they are.

B. Operational Criteria

Fishing operation shall:

12. make use of fishing gear and practices designed to avoid the capture of non-target species (and non-target size, age, and/or sex of the target species); minimise mortality of this catch where it cannot be avoided, and reduce discards of what cannot be released alive;

13. implement appropriate fishing methods designed to minimise adverse impacts on habitat, especially in critical or sensitive zones such as spawning and nursery areas;

14. not use destructive fishing practices such as fishing with poisons or explosives;

15. minimise operational waste such as lost fishing gear, oil spills, on-board spoilage of catch, etc.;

16. be conducted in compliance with the fishery management system and all legal and administrative requirements; and

17. assist and co-operate with management authorities in the collection of catch, discard, and other information of importance to effective management of the resources and the fishery.

Glossary & Acronyms

Glossary

Algal bloom - an abundant growth of phytoplankton, typically triggered by sudden favourable environmental conditions e.g. excess nutrients

Aquaculture is the general term given to the cultivation of any aquatic (fresh and marine) species (plant or animal)

Artisanal - term used to describe small-scale, traditional fisheries

Beam trawl - in this type of trawl the mouth of the net is kept open by a beam which is mounted at each end on guides or skids which travel along the seabed

Benthic - living on or in the seabed

Benthos - those organisms attached to, living on, or in the seabed

Berried or egg-bearing lobster or crab

Bioaccumulation - the accumulation of a substance within the tissues of an organism

Biodiversity - term used to express the variability amongst living organisms

Biomagnification - the process whereby concentrations of certain substances increase with each step in the food chain

Biomass - the total weight of living organisms or total weight of a resource or stock

Bivalve - having two shells or valves which open and shut

Boreal - living near the north; sub arctic

Bottom trawl is a large cone-shaped net, which is towed across the seabed

By-catch - non-target organisms caught in fishing gear

Caviar - the salted roes (eggs) of various fish, esp. the sturgeon

Cephalopod - a mollusc having a distinct head with prehensile and locomotive organs attached e.g. octopus, squid and cuttlefish

Cholesterol - substance found in animal tissue and fat

Cod-end - the rear end of a trawl where catch accumulates

Conservation measure - term applied to legislative methods within the framework of the CFP which regulate fishing activity

Conservative pollutants are permanent additions to the environment and not subject to decay

Coral – crab roe or eggs

Crustacea - hard-shelled animals e.g. crab, lobster

Decommission - term used to describe the process by which fishing boats are taken out of service or 'scrapped'

Deep-water species - those species living in water beyond the continental slope in depths of more than 400 metres

Demersal refers to fish such as cod, haddock and pollack which live primarily near the seabed

Diadromous fish - e.g. salmon and eels that move during their life cycle between fresh and marine waters

Dioxin - a group of chemical compounds

Discards - fish and other organisms caught by fishing gear and then thrown back into the sea for legal or economic or other reasons

Dredging is used for harvesting bivalve molluscs such as oysters, clams and scallops from the seabed

Ecosystem - a community of organisms and their physical environment interacting as an ecological unit

Ecosystem approach - the ecosystem approach to fisheries management involves a consideration of all the physical, chemical and biological variables within an ecosystem, taking account of their complex interactions

Elasmobranch - fish with out bones (sharks, skates and rays)

Eutrophication - the process whereby receiving waters become enriched by nutrient inputs resulting in excessive plant growth and oxygen depletion

Exclusive Economic Zone (EEZ) - an area in which a coastal state has sovereign rights over all the economic resources of the sea, seabed and subsoil

Extirpation - the loss of a local population as distinct from an entire species (extinction)

Fecundity - potential reproductive capacity of an organism or population expressed in number of eggs (fertile or not) produced during each reproductive cycle

Fish - collective term (includes molluscs and crustaceans) for any aquatic animal which is harvested

Fishery - the sum of all fishing activities on a given resource e.g. shrimp fishery or activity of catching fish from one or more stocks e.g. North Sea cod fishery or it may also refer to a single type or style of fishing e.g. trawl fishery

Fishing - any activity that involves the catching, taking or harvesting of fish

Fishing capacity - the quantity of fish that can be taken by a fishing unit i.e. individual, community, vessel or fleet

Fishing effort - the amount of fishing gear of a specific type used over a given unit of time e.g. hours trawled per day; the overall amount of fishing expressed in units of time e.g. number of hauls per boat per day

Food chain - representation of the passage of energy (food) from producers to the organisms that feed on them

Food web - network of food chains in an ecosystem

Gadiformes - the taxonomic Order which includes cod, pollack, whiting and haddock

Gadoid - see Gadiformes

Gear - any tools used to catch fish, such as hook and line, trawls, traps etc.

Ghost fishing - the term given to the phenomenon whereby lost nets or traps continue to fish

Gill net - a loosely set and near invisible wall of fine netting (mono or multi-filament nylon) that traps fish by the gill covers

Gonad - sex gland

Ground fish - American term for round or demersal fish

Handlining or hook and line fishing is a highly selective method of fishing producing high quality catch

Imposex - a condition in which the gender of an organism has become indeterminate as a result of hormonal imbalances or disruption, as in the case of the effect of tributyltin on gastropods

Industrial fisheries are fisheries which do not target species for direct human consumption

Long-lining - uses both vertical and horizontal lines often a number of miles long to which short lengths of line (snoods) carrying baited hooks are attached at intervals

Misreporting - false or incorrect reporting of details pertaining to quantity and area of capture of protected species i.e. those species regulated by quota

Mixed fishery - comprising more than one species e.g. demersal fisheries comprise cod, haddock, whiting, pollack and saithe

Mobile gear or active fishing gears e.g. trawl or purse seine nets

Multi-Annual Guidance Programme (MAGP) - programme to monitor progress towards reducing excess fishing effort throughout the European fleet

Otter board or door (originally wooden) used to spread the net mouth when net towed by one vessel

Otter trawl - see bottom or demersal trawl

Overcapacity - a state of saturation or an excess of productive capacity

Overfishing - fishing with a sufficiently high intensity to reduce the catch rates that a fish population should be capable of sustaining

Pelagic refers to fish such as herring, sardine and pilchard which live in the upper layers of the ocean where food is plentiful

Phylum – major taxonomic division of animals and plants that contain one or more classes

Phytoplankton - the plant component of the plankton

Pinger - acoustic device designed to deter entanglement of marine mammals in fishing nets

Plankton - those organisms (plant or animal) that are unable to maintain their position or distribution independent of the movement of the water

Pole and line hand held or mechanically operated rod with baited hook or lure

Pollution - the introduction by man, directly or indirectly, of substances or energy to the marine environment resulting in deleterious effects

Population - a biological unit representing the individuals of a species living in a specific area

Pot - a trap used to capture fish esp. shellfish

Purse seining is the general name given to the method of encircling a school of fish on or near the surface with a large wall of net

Quota - a share of the Total Allowable Catch (TAC) allocated to a country, vessel, company or individual fishermen

Recruitment - the process by which fish enter the exploitable stock and become susceptible to fishing

Round fish - fish that are rounded in transverse section (as opposed to flat fish e.g. plaice or flounder)

Safe Biological Limits - limits (reference points) for fishing mortality rates and spawning stock biomass, beyond which the fishery is unsustainable. Other criteria which indicate when a stock is outside safe biological limits include age structure and distribution of the stock and exploitation rates. A fishery which maintains stock size within a precautionary range (a range within which the probability of reaching any limits is very small) would be expected to be sustainable

Seamount - inactive underwater volcanoe

Selectivity - ability to target and capture fish by size and species, allowing by-catch of juvenile and non-target species to escape unharmed

Shellfish - collective term for molluscs and crustaceans

Spawn - release of ova (eggs) fertilized or to be fertilized

Spawning stock - mature part of a stock responsible for reproduction

Spawning Stock Biomass (SSB) - the total weight of all sexually mature fish in a population

Static or fixed gears refer to fishing gears e.g. pots, traps or nets that are fixed to or on the seabed. These type of gears are passive as opposed to mobile gears e.g. trawl nets which are referred to as active gears

Stock - term given to a group of individuals in a species occupying a well-defined spatial range independent of other stocks of the same species. A stock will form the basis of a distinct fishery defined in terms of season and area

Straddling stocks - fish stocks that migrate between EEZs

Sweep - the rope (usually wire) between the otter board and net

Tangle net - a type of gill net used to capture flatfish and crustaceans

Target species - species or assemblage of species which are primarily sought in a fishery

Teleost - bony fish as opposed to cartilaginous fish (elasmobranchs)

Total Allowable Catch (TAC) - maximum tonnage, set each year, that may be taken of a fish species within an area.

Trophic - pertaining to nutrition or steps in a food chain (levels)

Zooplankton - the animal component of plankton; animals suspended or drifting in the water column including larvae of many fish and benthic invertebrates

Acronyms

AIDCAP Agreement on the International Dolphin Conservation Programme
ASP Amnesic Shellfish Poisoning
CCAMLR Commission for the Conservation of Antarctic Marine Living Resources
CFFA Coalition for Fair Fisheries Agreements
CFP Common Fisheries Policy
CITES Convention on International Trade in Endangered Species
DARD Department of Agriculture and Rural Development
DEFRA Department for Environment, Food and Rural Affairs
DSP Diarrhoetic Shellfish Poisoning
EC European Commission
EEZ Exclusive Economic Zone
EFA Essential Fatty Acid
EIA Environmental Impact Assessment
EII Earth Island Institute
ENGO Environmental Non-Governmental Organisation
ETI Ethical Trade Initiative
ETP Eastern Tropical Pacific
EU European Union
FAO Food and Agriculture Organisation
FASF Frozen At Sea Fillets
FSA Food Standards Agency
GAA Global Aquaculture Alliance
GMO Genetically Modified Organism
IATCC Inter-American Tropical Tuna Commission
ICCAT International Commission for the Conservation of Atlantic Tuna
ICES International Council for the Exploration of the Sea
ICSF International Collective in Support of Fishworkers
ILO International Labour Organisation
IUCN World Conservation Union
IUU Illegal, Unreported and Unregulated fishing
IWC International Whaling Commission
MAFF Ministry of Agriculture Fisheries and Food (now DEFRA)
MAGP Multi-Annual Guidance Programme
MCS Marine Conservation Society
MLS Minimum Landing Size
MMS Minimum Mesh Size
MSC Marine Stewardship Council
NAWAD National Assembly for Wales Agriculture Department
NFFO National Federation of Fishermen's Organisations
NGO Non-Governmental Organisation
NTZ No Take Zone
PAH Polyaromatic Hydrocarbon
PCB Polychlorinated Biphenyl
PO Producer Organisation
PSP Paralytic Shellfish Poisoning
PUFA Polyunsaturated Fatty Acid
RFMO Regional Fisheries Management Organisation
RFO Regional Fisheries Organisation
SEERAD Scottish Executive Environment and Rural Affairs Department
SFC Sea Fisheries Committee
SFF Scottish Fishermen's Federation
SMP Square Mesh Panel
SQS Scottish Quality Salmon
TAC Total Allowable Catch
TBT Tributyltin
TED Turtle Excluder Device
UKROFS United Kingdom Register of Organic Food Standards
UNCED United Nations Committee on Environmental Development
UNCLOS United Nations Convention on Law Of the Sea
WHO World Health Organisation
WWF World Wide Fund for Nature

References &
Photo credits

References

Chapter one

A Dead-End for Deep-Water Fish?
Marine Conservation Society and Seas at
Risk (2001). Marine Conservation
Society, Ross-on-Wye, UK.

Key to the Fishes of Northern Europe.
A Wheeler (1978). Frederick Warne,
London.

Leiths Fish Bible.
CJ Jackson & C Waldegrave (1995).
Bloomsbury, London.

Major Market Trends, including the Impact
of Imports and the Competitive Edge of
Domestic Landings.
Seafish (1999). Seafish Industry
Authority, Edinburgh.

National Food Survey Report 2000.
DEFRA (2001). The Stationery Office.
London.

Rick Stein's Seafood Lover's Guide.
R Stein (2000). BBC Publications, London.

UK Sea Fisheries Statistics 1999 and 2000.
Editor David Lee (2001). Department for
Environment, Food and Rural Affairs
(DEFRA). The Stationery Office. London.
Fisheries Statistics Unit Tel: 020 7238
5913 fsu@fish.defra.gsi.gov.uk

United Kingdom Fish Industry Annual
Statistics 1999.
Seafish (2000). Sea Fish Industry
Authority, Edinburgh.

United Kingdom Fish Industry Annual
Statistics 2000.
Seafish (2001). Sea Fish Industry
Authority, Edinburgh. June 2001.

Chapter two

Consumers to get more info on fisheries
products. www.intrafish.com

Earth Island Institute www. Earthisland.org

Eco-labelling and sustainable fisheries.
CL Deere (1999). IUCN: Washington, DC
and FAO: Rome.

One in seven consumers say ethical concerns
influence decisions. ENDS (2000).
ENDS Report October 2000. London.

The State of World Fisheries and
Aquaculture 2000.
FAO Fisheries Department. FAO Rome
2000.

Chapter three

http://europa.eu

Key to the Fishes of Northern Europe.
A Wheeler (1978). Frederick Warne,
London.

Leiths Fish Bible.
CJ Jackson & C Waldegrave (1995).
Bloomsbury, London.

Living Marine Molluscs.
CM Yonge & TE Thompson (1976). Collins,
London.

Marine Wildlife of Atlantic Europe.
A Young (1994). Immel Publishing, London.

The Edible Crab and its fishery in British
Waters.
E Edwards (1979) Fishing News Books
Ltd. Surrey.

The Hamlyn Guide to Seashores & Shallow
Seas of Britain and Europe.
AC Campbell (1976). Hamlyn, London.

The Kind Food Guide.
Audrey Eyton. (out of print).

UK Biodiversity Action Plan – Native Oyster
Species Information Review 2001.
English Nature (2001)., English Nature.
Peterborough, UK.

www.fishbase.org

www.ices.org

Chapter four

Commercial Fishing Methods. An
introduction to vessels and gears.
Third Edition. John C Sainsbury (1996).
Fishing News Books.